Inclined Planes
in the South West

A gazetteer of selected sites in Somerset, Dorset, Devon and Cornwall

Martin Bodman

TWELVEHEADS PRESS

TRURO   2012

TWELVEHEADS PRESS

First published 2012 by Twelveheads Press.
ISBN 978 0 906294 75 8
British Library Cataloguing-in-Publication Data.
A catalogue record for this book is available from the British Library.
Typeset in Frutiger
Printed by Tower Print Ltd, South Wales

Contents

Acknowledgements 4

Preface 5

Introduction 7

    The inclined plane - a short history 8

    Inclined plane designers 11

Gazetteer 14

    Section 1:   The Bristol Avon 16

    Section 2:   North and North-east Somerset 22

    Section 3:   Somerset: the Mendips to the Blackdowns 31

    Section 4:   Dorset and East Devon 38

    Section 5:   Exmoor, North Devon and Lundy 44

    Section 6:   Dartmoor 56

    Section 7:   South Devon and South-west Dartmoor 64

    Section 8:   The Lower Tamar Valley 70

    Section 9:   North and East Cornwall 80

    Section 10: Mid Cornwall 88

    Section 11: West Cornwall 100

Glossary 107

References 109

Bibliography 115

Index 120

FRONT COVER: The Portreath Incline. *Pope/Parkhouse Archive*
East Cliff Railway, Bournemouth. *Richard and Gill Long*
BACK COVER: Map: Brendon Hill Iron Mines. *Somerset Industrial Archaeology Society*
Portrait: William Reynolds by Hobday. *Ironbridge Gorge Museum Trust*
Top: Brendon Hill Iron Mines. *Somerset Industrial Archaeology Society*
Bottom: Kelly Mine, in Bovey Tracey parish, near Lustleigh. *KH, Mine-Explorer*

Acknowledgements

Many individuals have given me considerable help in compiling this volume. In particular my thanks go to my publisher Michael Messenger for encouraging me to undertake the project and for suggesting sites and providing images; to Brian Murless and Geoff Roughton for finding numerous additional sites; to Barry Hughes for providing his drawings of the planes at Ridd and Hobbacott, for offering photographs and detailed information on sites in North Devon and for allowing me to quote a passage from his book *The Rolle Canal and the North Devon Lime Trade*. I am also particularly grateful to Phil Newman and Doug Westaway for very useful material relating to Dartmoor sites, and likewise to Robert Waterhouse for texts and images relating to sites in the lower Tamar valley. Shane Gould has kindly provided advice on sites in the Somerset coalfield.

For contributions to the Somerset, Dorset and Bristol Avon sections, I'm also grateful for contributions from Mike Chapman, Geoff Fitton, David Greenwood, Paul Gregory, Ken Kemp, Bill Morris of the National Trust, Dylan Moore, Maggie Shapland, Diane Stewart, Chris Tilley, Alan Tucker, Adrian Tuddenham and staff at the Portland Heritage Centre. In Devon, I'd also like to thank Ashley Clarke, of the Lynton & Lynmouth Cliff Railway Company, and Rick Stewart.

In Cornwall I have received help from Clive Benney, Bryn Tapper, Colin Buck and John R Smith of Cornwall Council, Simon Burgess of Poynton Bradbury Wynter Cole Architects Ltd, Craig Brown of Alimak Hek Ltd, Dave Cooper of LECS UK, Maurice Dart, Lynda Harman of Calstock Archive, Helen Harris, Joanne Laing of the Cornish Studies Library, Sarah Lloyd-Durrant at the Royal Cornwall Museum, Pete Joseph, Martin Watts, Lynda White of the British Geological Survey, Robin Whalley, and Colin Vallance of the Wheal Martyn China Clay Museum.

I am indebted to Brian Murless, Michael Messenger, Geoff Roughton and Ric Auger, for casting critical eyes over various drafts. Brian Murless also assisted with mapping and I owe especial thanks to Jon Webb for creating maps for a significant number of the sites; where, for one reason or another, the route of a tramway, railway or canal was not clearly delineated on an Ordnance Survey edition.

While I have endeavoured to ensure texts are readable and at the same time as accurate as possible, this volume covers new ground and there will inevitably be some errors. I can only apologise when these occur.

Photographs and other images

My thanks go to several photographers I came across on the Flickr web site, and others on the Geograph site, who have supplemented photographs from museums and collections with very useful present-day views of surviving planes and related sites.

The map relating to the Treffry Viaduct temporary inclined plane, is reproduced with the following acknowledgement: 'Extract from the Luxulyan Valley survey undertaken as part of An Archaeological and Historical Survey (Cornwall Archaeological Unit, 1988). Plan 10, SX 055570, 1:2500. © Historic Environment Service, Cornwall Council 2011.'

The Delabole Quarry and Lantern China Clay Pit images are reproduced by permission of the British Geological Survey © NERC. All rights reserved.

Photographs of the West Cliff Railway, Bournemouth, the Babbacombe Cliff Lift, Torquay, and the reversal on the Steep Holm inclined planes are reproduced under a Creative Commons Licence.

Preface

I first became aware of cable-operated inclined planes over fifty years ago, when taking a trip on Bergen's Fløibanen. A year or so later, I came to appreciate that the inclined plane was a standard feature in many Welsh slate quarries. In recent decades I came across several significant survivals in the south west. My aim in compiling this gazetteer has been to bring together the available information on known sites. I'm not an engineer, nor an archaeologist, although I have worked with engineers and published and promoted their skills for much of my career.

Others have made significant contributions to the history of the inclined plane in the south west. A monograph by Helen Harris and Monica Ellis led the way with *The Bude Canal* and its planes in 1972. More recently Barry Hughes has contributed to our understanding of the Rolle Canal and the working of its incline at Ridd. Mike Jones, an architect, has now published an impressive work: *The Brendon Hills Iron Mines and The West Somerset Mineral Railway, A New Account*, (2011), which goes into considerable detail on the construction of the railway's inclined plane. Robert Waterhouse, who is an archaeologist, has a forthcoming volume on the Tavistock Canal and the planes associated with that endeavour; the result of nine years research.

The gazetteer is an overview. I also attempt to record some of the sites that have been lost. Jones and Waterhouse show what can be done in making detailed recordings of a segment of our industrial and transport history in the south west that has not always received the attention that it merits. Inclined planes remain as features in our landscape; some are accessible to the public whilst others await discovery.

Introduction

The south western counties of England are rich in industrial archaeological sites: much of this history has been published. Many of these publications have been devoted to railways; several purely to industrial railways. This is possibly the first to focus specifically on the inclined plane.

The impressive inclined plane at Hobbacott, North Cornwall, once part of the Bude Canal. It functioned from 1825 until 1891. Also known as the Thurlibeer Incline, it now forms part of 'The Planekeeper's Path', with public access allowed. This view dates from the 1970s. *Helen Harris*

From the dawn of the nineteenth century until the middle of the twentieth the cable-worked inclined plane was the best available engineering solution at many sites where goods had to be raised or lowered to a river quay or tramway, road, railway or canal.

Mining and quarrying have taken place mainly in upland landscapes, and the south west has an extensive coastline and many sea cliffs. This topography has posed challenges for engineers and industrialists intent on transporting or shipping ores to smelters or stone for buildings, lighthouses and quays. At the same time landowners sought to import sea sand via canals to improve the poor soils in parts of Devon and Cornwall.

Some inclines are major engineering endeavours and their formations survive in the landscape today. The Brendon Hill Incline on the West Somerset Mineral Railway is one example; the Portreath Incline on the Hayle Railway another. The canal inclines at Hobbacott and Marhamchurch are also notable. The incline on the Merchants Railway, Isle of Portland, operated for over one hundred years, from 1826 to 1939. Mention should also be made of the Carmears Incline in the Luxulyan valley.

Some inclined planes may gain protection now that they are situated within the Cornwall and West Devon Mining Landscape, designated a World Heritage Site in July 2006. St Just in Penwith, Trewavas, Portreath Harbour, St Agnes, the Luxulyan Valley, the Caradon district, Tavistock and the Tamar valley feature.

These and planes at many other locations are included here. This is not a definitive record: that is beyond the scope of this publication. The gazetteer provides a guide to 220 inclines. Some no longer exist, some are inaccessible — are on private land — but other impressive sites, such as those mentioned above, can be viewed and in some cases walked over.

The inclined plane – a short history

The inclined plane was in use from the mid eighteenth century and more recent examples still function today.

Transport systems developed rapidly from the mid eighteenth century onwards. In that century the canal became the main trunk route. The railway began as a wooden tramroad; a feeder serving the waterways. The south west features much upland topography, where mining and quarrying were undertaken. Initially inclined planes were used to link mines and quarries in the hills with navigable rivers.

Many of the inclined planes recorded here worked on the counter-balanced principle. In simple terms the plane would consist of two parallel rail tracks, typically on a slope of 1 in 4, on which wagons were conveyed. These wagons would be linked together by a continuous rope or cable or chain which was passed round a drum at the incline head or summit. The weight of a loaded truck or trucks descending the plane was sufficient to draw an empty truck or trucks up. A brakesman would control the descent at the incline head. The drum incorporated a brake to control the speed of descent and ascent.

Canal inclines and their alternatives

Canals were designed for barges, which are unsuitable for inclines. So where an inclined plane was introduced on a canal system, trans-shipment was required; it was cumbersome and inefficient. In Shropshire early canals used tub-boats, much smaller vessels, that could be carried over the incline, eliminating the need to transfer cargoes. These were carried on cradles, similar to those used on the Welsh slate industry inclines.

There were alternatives: locks were used to raise a canal, but a flight of locks was needed to gain appreciable height. However, locks need a good water supply, which may not always be available. The canal lift, another alternative, was rarely adopted and merely raised a canal perhaps 30 feet rather than the typical 10 feet of a canal lock.

A further approach to freight transfer between different levels on a canal was the tunnel-and-shaft system. A tunnel from the lower level of the canal would be cut into a hill, its underground terminus connected by a shaft or pair of shafts with the canal above. Freight would be raised or lowered using a self-acting system, employing gravity. William Reynolds was responsible for one such site at Brierly Hill, on an arm of the Shropshire Canal. It was used from July 1791 until the autumn of 1793. Such a solution was expensive to construct and involved trans-shipment underground. No examples survive.

Nevertheless, the concept did find a use on some of the longer canal inclines, as a means of providing power. As a large bucket or cylinder, filled with water, descended the shaft, its weight was used to haul tub boats up the incline; its water released into the tunnel or adit at the foot

The framework of a disused brake drum at the head of a single-track slate quarry incline in North Wales. *D. Sallery*

of the shaft. This system was used successfully on the Hobbacott incline on the Bude Canal.

The self-acting inclined plane was not always achievable and in many cases motive power in addition to gravity was required to raise wagons or tub boats up an inclined plane. Water power was often the prime mover for earlier inclines. On smaller planes a horse gin might suffice. As technology developed, steam power came into its own, and was adopted to power inclined planes.

Canal inclines called for cutting edge technology as cast-iron machinery was required to transfer the power from a waterwheel to the headgear at the incline summit. The use of iron gear trains was a late eighteenth century development, occurring at the same time as water-powered factories were becoming established in Yorkshire, using similar technology.

This machinery called for skilled men to run and maintain the inclines: the incline keepers would ideally have had a background in millwrighting.

Wood and rope, iron and steel

In time the feeder tramways took on a life of their own: canals became redundant and the railway age dawned. Early railways relied on inclined planes as it was thought steam locomotives lacked the adhesive power needed on inclines steeper than 1 in 80. Civil engineers became more assured and in time inclines were bypassed with tunnels and viaducts. Steam engines increased in power and were able to climb gradients up to 1 in 30. A typical inclined plane had a gradient of 1 in 4.

Many cable-worked inclines formed part of a conventional railway, connected at head and foot to horse-drawn or locomotive-hauled lines. But others were self contained, such as the cliff railways. Here the cable car (or wagon) is permanently fixed to the cable and the system is known as a funicular.

Whereas inclined planes serving canals tended to employ chain haulage, inclines on railways often operated with ropes.

Broad-gauge cradles carrying narrow gauge slate trucks on an incline in North Wales. The cradle with the loaded trucks raises the one with the empties. Drum or winding house beyond. *D. Sallery*

Chains were subject to break and ropes had limited strength. In 1825 rope used on railway inclines was typically specified as '6 inch'; it weighed 4 tons a mile and cost £50 a ton. It had a diameter of just under two inches. Such rope allowed a safe working load of a little over three tons.

Ropes limited the length of inclines and on a long descent it was deemed necessary to divide the plane into two halves, or even into three sections, each with its own drumhouse at the summit. Long gravity inclines only became reliable with the invention of steel wire reinforced ropes. Wilhelm Albert, a German mining engineer, produced the forerunner of modern wire ropes in 1831-1834.

Wooden tramroads gave way to cast iron tramways. Cast iron

plates were first made at Coalbrookdale, Shropshire, in 1767 and used to face wooden rails. But it was 1789 before cast iron rails were used. Rolled wrought iron rails were introduced by John Birkinshaw in Northumberland in 1820. Robert Mushet originated the steel rail in 1857 and this material came to be universally adopted on railways, being far more durable than the alternatives.

Nineteenth century developments – narrow gauge railways

The success of narrow-gauge railways in upland districts, such as the Ffestiniog in north Wales – built to the 1ft 11½in gauge and opened in 1836 – led to a profusion of railways in mines and quarries from the mid-nineteenth century onwards. Narrow-gauge track was much cheaper and easier to lay than standard gauge track, particularly in difficult terrain. The use of inclined planes, often worked by gravity, became an established feature in these industries.

Towards the end of the nineteenth century the twin-track inclined plane was seen to be an extravagance and the layout was often simplified. A single track would run from the foot of the plane to a passing loop half way up the plane. The top section would be laid as three rail, so that the cable end linked to the ascending wagon was kept separate from the end attached to the descending one.

As the end of the century neared, tourism, aided by the spread of the railway system, was becoming increasingly popular. And in this environment the seaside cliff railway made its appearance. The south western counties have several, still in operation.

In the twentieth century inclined planes continued to find use in quarries and mines. But the plane was now giving way to other transport systems. The Blondin was adopted by some quarries. This was a type of aerial cableway or bucketway, which typically linked the quarry face to the crusher plant. More importantly, the rise of the internal combustion engine meant that the dumper truck or lorry could transport stone, slate or ore from the quarry or mine to wherever it was required far more efficiently than a railway which involved inclined plane working.

The inclined plane hasn't become completely redundant. The cliff railways still run in season and just before the millennium the RNLI introduced a new plane to provide access to its lifeboat station at Kilcobben Cove, on the Lizard. This was updated in 2011. A similar installation was modified for the Padstow lifeboat station in 2008-9, although this is now a rack-and-pinion type.

Inclined plane designers

William Reynolds

William Reynolds (1758-1803) was born at Ketley, Shropshire, in April 1758. His father was a Bristolian. A maternal grandfather was Abraham Darby (1711-1763). Shropshire was the leading iron-producing county of England at the time and Reynolds was to become one of the leading ironmasters of his day. He was the founder of Coalport and an associate of Erasmus Darwin. The tub boat canals of the east Shropshire coalfield were largely developed on his initiative. In 1788 Reynolds supervised the construction of the first successful canal inclined plane at Ketley. It was worked by gravity and had twin tracks. [1]

His success with the Ketley plane led to the construction of the Hay inclined plane, Coalport, opened in 1793. It has a vertical rise of 207 ft and is double-track, terminating in a canal basin at its summit. It was also self-acting and, like the Ketley plane, employed cradles to carry the tub boats, but here the stationary steam engine at its head was attached to the winding drum, to haul the boats up the 1 in 4 gradient from the Severn valley when there was no compensating downward load. Hay differed from the plane at Ketley in one other key aspect. The twin rail tracks at the summit were taken down a reverse slope into water-filled docks on the Shropshire Canal, allowing the tub boats to float off their cradles into the canal, without the need for a lock. This arrangement subsequently became a standard feature on many canal inclined planes. Its designers were Henry Williams and John Lowdon. [2]

Reynolds' use of tub boats and inclined planes was seen and praised by Robert Fulton. In turn Fulton's influence led to the construction of tub boat canals in the south west, designed by James Green. Reynolds may also have had some influence on the design of inclined planes in the Somerset coalfield; feeders to the Coal Canal. Samborn Palmer, a coal proprietor, and a member of the Somersetshire Coal Canal Committee, visited Shropshire in 1791 and toured Reynolds' Ketley Works. He would have seen the Ketley plane and his diary shows a clear interest in canal lift technology. [3]

Reynolds by Hobday. An inclined plane can be seen in the landscape beyond.
Ironbridge Gorge Museum Trust

Hay inclined plane: at its head the rails used to run back on a short reverse plane into the canal. *Calotype46, Flickr*

Robert Fulton. *Science Photo Library*

John Taylor. *Science Photo Library*

Robert Fulton

The American, Robert Fulton (1765-1815), is known for the design of steamboats, the first practical submarine and torpedoes. He was also involved in the development of tub-boat canals and a was promoter of the inclined plane.

In 1796 he published a report for Sir Francis Buller on the proposed Helston Canal, linking the rivers Hayle and Helford, so avoiding the dangerous passage around Land's End. The scheme would have involved seven planes but was never built.[4] In the same year he also published 'A Treatise on the Improvement of Canal Navigation'; this was prompted by an early scheme for the Bude Canal, promoted by the Earl of Stanhope. In it he praised William Reynolds as a genius, for successfully introducing tub boat canals, using 5 ton tub boats instead of conventional 25 ton barges, enabling the boats to travel over inclined planes. He also proposed the bucket-in-the-well system for powering longer canal inclines; a concept later adopted by James Green on the Bude Canal for one of its inclines.

John Taylor

John Taylor (1779-1863) was a leading nineteenth century mining entrepreneur and engineer. He was born in Norfolk but by 1796 was at work on the Wheal Friendship near Tavistock. Two years later he was running the copper mine, aged nineteen.

His next major project was the Tavistock Canal, which involved the construction of a mile-and-a-half-long tunnel under Morwell Down, to link Tavistock with the river Tamar. In the Tamar valley the canal and quays at Morwellham were linked by an inclined plane. Taylor was also responsible for the design of Wheal Crebor which involved an underground incline with its summit within the Morwell Down canal tunnel. A great exponent of water power, he introduced two further inclined planes in tunnel at the Wheal Friendship mine at Mary Tavy, his original mining operation in Devon. It is conceivable that the water-powered limekiln banks at Tavistock – now demolished – and Morwellham Quay were also to his desgn. He was later one of the founders of University College, London.

James Green

Canal development in the south west was taken forward by James Green (1781-1849), a protege of John Rennie. He was responsible for the following canal projects:
– Bude Canal, designed in 1817-18, with six inclined planes, using tub boats over most of its length
– Rolle Canal, another tub boat canal, connecting Torrington with Bideford, with an inclined plane at Ridd
– Grand Western Canal, linking Tiverton with Taunton, involving seven lifts and an inclined plane at Wellisford
– Initial design of the Chard Canal, linking Chard with the Bridgwater and Taunton Canal.
He was promoting canals after the railway age had arrived, but failed to embrace it.

Joseph Thomas Treffry

J. T. Treffry, (1782-1850), born Joseph Austen and son of a Plymouth brewer, inherited the Treffry estate at Fowey in 1808. Educated at Oxford and trained in civil engineering, Treffry was a mining adventurer and industrialist famous for

Joseph Thomas Treffry.
Wheal Martyn Museum/China Clay History Society

the Treffry Viaduct in the Luxulyan valley; and together with his agent William Pease, he is known to have constructed or planned eight inclined planes in mid-Cornwall.[5] These were:

• Fowey Consols to the Par Canal, 1829, 1834 (two planes)
• Par Consols to his harbour at Par, 1841
• Treffry viaduct construction incline, c 1842
• Carmears, on the Treffry Tramway, 1842
• Caffa Mill Pill, Fowey, 1844
• Newquay Harbour, 1846
• Hendra Downs, 1857 - completed after his death.

Three of these planes were worked by water-power, for which Treffry was a noted advocate. The Carmears plane linked the upper level of the Treffry tramway with Ponts Mill, and was part of a system carrying granite, china clay and minerals to Par harbour.

George Croydon Marks

George Croydon Marks, later The Lord Marks (1858-1938), was an engineer and politician. He gained experience with funicular lifts working for Sir Richard Tangye; an early project involved the design and installation of the Saltburn Cliff Lift, near Redcar. This was completed in 1884. It was the forerunner of the Lynton-Lynmouth Cliff Railway: both use the water counter-balance principle.

Later, in partnership with newspaper magnate Sir George Newnes, Marks planned an outline scheme for Babbacombe, Torquay. This was followed in 1888 by the Lynton-Lynmouth project, which opened in 1890. The Clifton Rocks Railway, constructed in tunnel, was also on his drawing board in 1888. It opened in 1893.

In 1906 Marks was elected Liberal Member of Parliament for the Launceston and North Cornwall constituency; he was knighted in 1911. He worked for the Ministry of Munitions during World War I. In 1929 he joined the Labour Party and was raised to the peerage. Other cliff railways designed by Marks included those at Bridgnorth and Aberystwyth. [6]

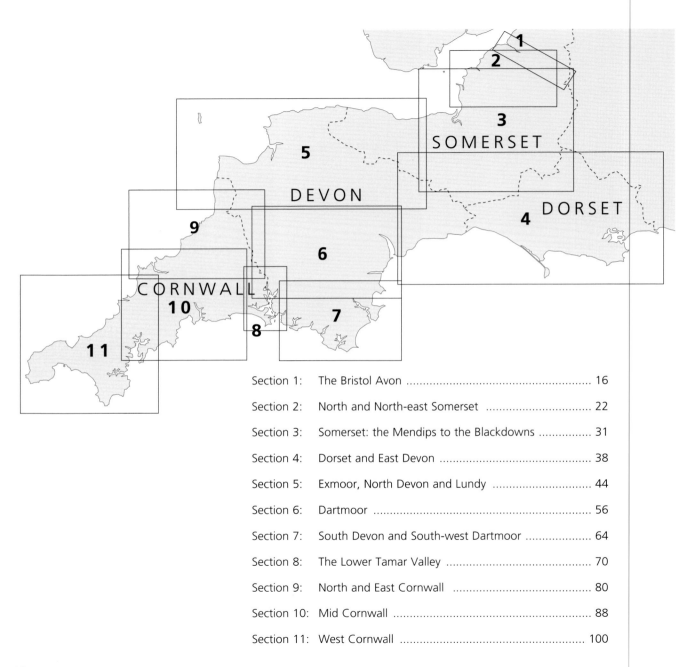

Section 1:   The Bristol Avon 16

Section 2:   North and North-east Somerset 22

Section 3:   Somerset: the Mendips to the Blackdowns 31

Section 4:   Dorset and East Devon 38

Section 5:   Exmoor, North Devon and Lundy 44

Section 6:   Dartmoor 56

Section 7:   South Devon and South-west Dartmoor 64

Section 8:   The Lower Tamar Valley 70

Section 9:   North and East Cornwall 80

Section 10: Mid Cornwall 88

Section 11: West Cornwall 100

Gazetteer

Quarries and mines provided the south west with many of its inclined planes. This example is the shorter of the two cable-worked inclines associated with the De Lank Quarry, St Breward, North Cornwall. It brought standard-gauge railway wagons right into the quarry workings. Here the passing loop merges to become three-rail formation below the drum or winding house.
Charles Daniel Collection

The following sections provide an outline record of inclined planes in the four historic counties that constitute the south west: Somerset, Dorset, Devon and Cornwall. Modern administrations – North Somerset and Bath & North-east Somerset are included. A few sites across the borders in South Gloucestershire and in Wiltshire have been added to complete the narrative.

The listings are not claimed to be definitive. Certain sites have been deliberately excluded and these are:

- underground planes or inclined shafts, with a few notable exceptions
- almost all planes serving china clay sky tips; a few samples are listed here:

- the Purbeck sled inclines
- most of the inclined planes in claypits serving brickworks
- short ramps exclusively on trestles in mines and quarries; other surface inclines at mines and quarries are recorded where known, and a few longer inclines on trestles noted. However, short powered planes serving limekilns are included; one or two of these were constructed on trestles
- patent slipways serving shipyards and lifeboat stations

The lengths, heights and gradients of most of the planes are, in many cases, as far as possible, good approximations rather than precise data. Maps are generally orientated with north at the top. In the text 'plane' and 'incline' are used as shorthand for 'inclined plane'.

The Bristol Avon

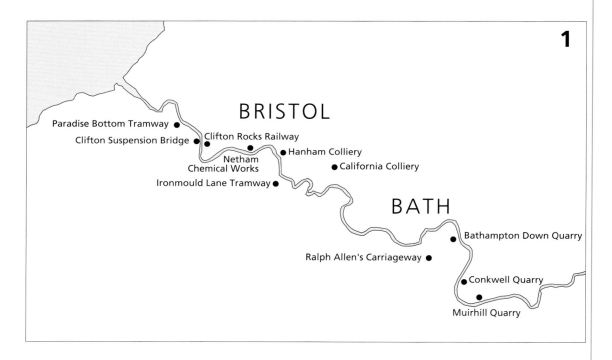

Bath is notable for having the first inclined tramway in the south west. Its creator, Ralph Allen, also assisted in making the river Avon navigable from its tidal limit at Hanham Mills, Bristol to Bath. The navigation opened in 1727. His carriageway opened in 1730. Stone from his quarries was then shipped by the plane and the river not only to Bath but also to Bristol and even to Dublin.

Quarry inclines, to the east of Bath, later aided the creation of the Kennet and Avon Canal, opened in 1810.

In 1836 Brunel used a temporary plane to haul materials up from the Avon to enable construction of the abutment for the Leigh Woods tower of the Clifton Suspension Bridge.

Two Bristol collieries later used planes to ship their coal out by river. The Clifton Rocks Railway, Bristol, also features, as does an incline at Brislington, where a few plate rails still exist in situ.

Bathampton Down Quarry, Bathampton
ST 783659 FOOT – ST 777653 HEAD

A plane from Bathampton Down Quarry to the Kennet and Avon Canal, was at work in 1810 and was 2,400 feet long with a descent of about 500 feet. It terminated at a wharf on the canal near Holcombe Farm, at the end of Holcombe Lane, north-east of the Bath-Warminster road, which it crossed on an overbridge. The overbridge was demolished in the 1960s when the road was widened. [1]

Pierce Egan saw the plane at work in 1819 as he walked the canal towpath towards Bath:

'...on the left hand side of which an iron rail-way, from an immense steep height is to be seen. It is curious to observe the iron carriages sent up and down, without horses; and by the aid of machinery the vehicles change their positions midway, the full one running down to the barge in the canal, and the empty one taking its way to the top again to receive its load.' [2]

It was a plateway. A public footpath now runs down most of the route.

California Colliery, Oldland
ST 668709 FOOT – ST 667709 HEAD

This mine was developed by Abraham Fussell in 1876. In 1881 it was connected to the then derelict Dramway by a 1 in 10, self-acting, incline. The Dramway ran to Londonderry Wharf on the Avon where coal was trans-shipped to barges taking the fuel to Bristol. The route was abandoned in 1904 after a flood inundated the colliery workings. A public footpath runs along the Dramway, close to the site. A large stone bridge, taking the incline over a river, survives at the foot of the formation. [3]

Clifton Rocks Railway, Bristol
ST 566730

One of the earliest cliff railways in the country, designed by George Croydon Marks in 1888. Like his cliff railway at Lynton this line was worked by water balance, but in other respects it differed. It was more ambitious. The line was almost entirely in tunnel and the gauge was 3 foot 2 inches. Four rail tracks

Clifton Rocks Railway, Bristol. *Clifton Rocks Railway Trust*

were laid; each pair of cars were connected by cable via a drum at the incline head and only one pair was worked at a time; the second pair was held in reserve. It ran from the Hotwells Road, by the spa, to Zion Hill, Clifton and was 500 feet long on a gradient of 1 in 2.2. Each car could carry 18 passengers and the journey time was 40 seconds. The railway was opened in March 1893; construction was delayed by unexpected faults in the rock strata through which the 28-foot-wide tunnel was bored. In 1912 Bristol Tramways Company bought the enterprise but passenger numbers fell and the railway closed in 1934. Running costs were higher than at Lynton: two gas engines had been installed to recycle the water from the descending car, when it reached the foot of the plane, to a reservoir at Zion Hill. The tunnel was used as an air raid shelter in World War II. [4]

A group of volunteers acted to form the Clifton Rocks Railway Trust in 2008. Their objective is to restore elements of the railway and they have the support of Bristol City Council and other bodies.

Clifton Suspension Bridge abutment, Leigh Woods, Long Ashton
ST 564730

A temporary inclined plane was employed by Isambard Kingdom Brunel's contractors to raise stone from barges on the river Avon, to enable construction of the Leigh Woods abutment, built in red sandstone in 1836. Contemporary reports suggest the incline was worked by two horse gins or whims. The project ran out of money and the iconic bridge was not completed until after Brunel's death in 1859. [5]

Right: the Avon valley near Limpley Stoke, showing the route of the Kennet and Avon Canal and the quarry inclines at Conkwell and Muirhill – both just in Wiltshire – linking to it. *Mike Chapman*
Below: Conkwell inclined plane in the twenty-first century, accessible as a public footpath. *Somerset Coal Canal Society*

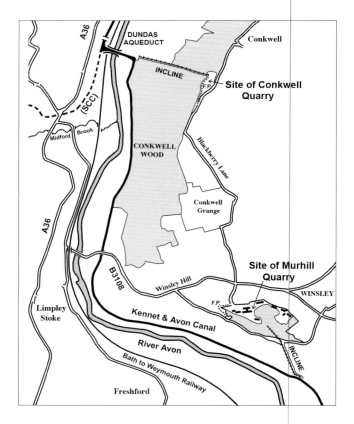

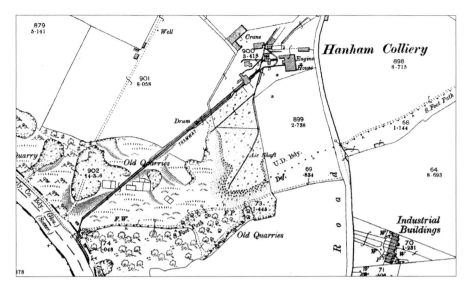

Hanham Colliery incline in 1904. The plane linked the mine with a wharf on the river Avon. From the Ordnance Survey 1:2,500 map. *Old-Maps*

Hanham Colliery incline in 2010.
Ken Kemp

Conkwell quarry incline, Winsley
ST 786625 FOOT – ST 78826244 HEAD

The construction of the Kennet and Avon Canal required quantities of stone for its aqueducts and bridges. A double-track self-acting inclined plane from Conkwell quarry in Winsley parish – just over the border, in Wiltshire – to a wharf by Dundas Aqueduct was operating from 1800 to 1812. It was a rope-worked plane, 1,635 feet long with a gradient of 1 in 5. The stone was found to be defective and by 1803 Rennie was advising the canal company to use brick as an alternative. [6]

Hanham Colliery, Hanham
ST 63487183 FOOT, BY WHARF – ST 63637196 HEAD

A twin track incline, about 690 foot long, formed the lower end of a tramway to a wharf on the river Avon. It ran by old quarry workings on a gradient of 1 in 5 and was in use in 1882-9: the incline drum is shown on the Ordnance Survey maps of the period. By 1904 sidings had been laid in above the drum house. The mine and tramway closed in 1926 when owned by East Bristol Collieries Limited; the site is now very wooded. A path existed on the formation in 1987 and it is still accessible today, partly in cutting. [7]

Ironmould Lane incline, Brislington
ST 63527077 FOOT – ST 63407067 HEAD (ESTIMATED)

An inclined plane powered by a horse whim, used at the outset – circa 1800 – for the haulage of construction materials from the Avon to Ironmould Lane for use at Brislington House, an institution for the mentally ill. Stone setts and some plate rails are still in situ at the point where the incline passes under the arched embankment of the London-Bristol main line; these survivals are suffering damage from overflowing ballast from the line above and from water ingress from a stream. The rest of the formation sees use as a footpath; its summit was about 135 to 140 feet above the river wharf. Following construction of the building the plane was used to take supplies to the institution. [8]

Muirhill quarry incline, Winsley

ST 79606048 WHARF – ST 795607 HEAD

An 850-foot-long incline, linking Muirhill quarry with the Kennet and Avon Canal, was constructed in 1803. This incline used wooden rails. A realigned route, with cast iron rails, operated from about 1826 and survived for some years. Track gauge on the later route was about 4 feet. The route has since been tarmaced and now serves as a road, still known as the 'Trolley Road'. [9]

Netham Chemical Works, Bristol

ST 61387271 FOOT – ST 61447284 HEAD (ESTIMATED)

This was a greenfield site in 1840; the factory was established by 1859. By 1883 the plant was manufacturing caustic soda, quicklime and sulphuric acid. A twin track incline, 450 feet long, linked the Feeder Canal with the works high on the bank above. At the foot of the incline, by the quay, the tramway served a limekiln. Hoppers carrying limestone ..

'.. moved up the 150 yard long incline to the crushing mills, all driven by steam. Carbonate of soda was manufactured by mixing salt cake with the crushed limestone and small coal in a large revolving furnace, fusing it into a molten mass. When it had cooled it was placed with black ash in iron tanks, the soda dissolved and the greenish chemical water left treated for the recovery of the soda.'

It is thought coal from a local mine went down the incline to serve the kiln, with some of the crushed limestone. Closure came in 1949. The works has long since gone and the site has been landscaped and is now a recreation ground.[10]

Paradise Bottom Tramway, Abbots Leigh

ST 54827518 FOOT – ST 54547486 HEAD (ESTIMATED)

R. B. Withers of Pill started to quarry celestine (strontium sulphate) on the Leigh Court estate in about 1880. A tramway, which may have been built in 1795, was rebuilt on the 2 foot gauge, with an inclined plane, taking the ore to Miles Dock, on the river Avon. The dock was named after William Miles of Leigh Court. It had originally been constructed to tranship stone to build the mansion.

A brakesman reputedly rode with a set of four side-tipping wagons, controlling their descent on the single-track incline. There must have been a stationary steam engine at the incline's summit to bring empty wagons up from the dock, unless perhaps there was a passing loop on the incline and it was worked by gravity.

The Bristol Strontia Company ran the quarries until closure in 1912: ninety per cent of the world's output of celestine came from the Bristol region at this time.[11]

The route of the tramway lies in Leigh Woods, now part of the National Trust estate, and is accessible by the public.

Paradise Bottom Tramway – the course of the incline in 2011. It linked celestine quarries near Leigh Court with Miles Dock by the river Avon. It is now accessible, within the National Trust's Leigh Woods estate.

Ralph Allen's Tramway, Bath

ST 755643 FOOT – ST 761627 HEAD

Ralph Allen (c1693-1764), a Cornishman and native of St Columb, pioneer of the eighteenth-century postal system, employed Bristol engineer John Padmore to design a wooden tramway from his stone quarries on Combe Down to a wharf on the river Avon in Bath. It operated from 1730 until his death. The gradient was 1 in 10, the descent 500 feet, the line about a mile and a half in all. The rail gauge was 3 feet 9 inches. Loaded trucks descended the single track under gravity, controlled by brakesmen walking alongside and horses were used to haul the empty wagons uphill.[12]

Allen's tramway was not a inclined plane in the form later adopted in the south west: while it used gravity, it was not self-acting, twin-track or cable operated. But it was the first known railway or tramway incline in the region. Its construction was influenced by the wooden wagonways developed by colliers on Tyneside.[13] The present day Prior Park Road and Ralph Allen Drive mark much of its course.

This tramway can be seen as a forerunner; it may well have encouraged the construction of the later cable-worked planes at Bathampton, Conkwell and Muirhill.

Ralph Allen's tramway ran from quarries at Combe Down to the river Avon at Bath, past his mansion at Prior Park. It functioned from 1730-1764. The wagons were used to carry Bath stone. The tramway and a crane by the river Avon, used to transfer the stone, were designed by John Padmore, a Bristol engineer. *Bath in Time - Bath Central Library*

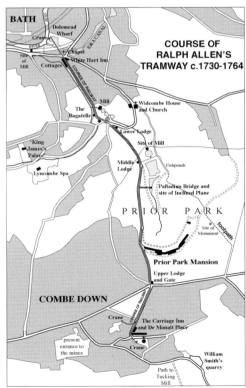

The tramway's route in Bath. *Mike Chapman*

North and North-east Somerset

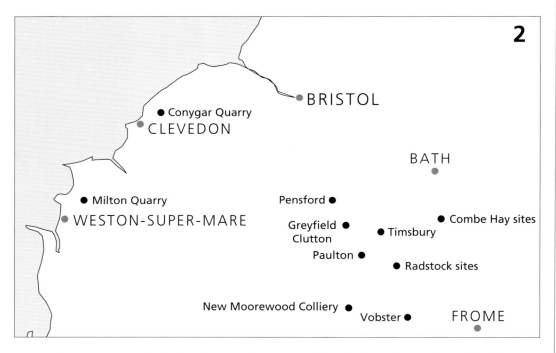

This section covers the county south of the Avon and embraces the Somerset coalfield, which extends onto the Mendips. Bath and Bristol are represented in the Bristol Avon section.

Almost all the inclined planes listed here were associated with the delivery of coal to Bath and points east. The Somersetshire Coal Canal was the catalyst: many of the mine inclines served it, or wagons on its Radstock tramway. The canal itself required an inclined plane, after the failure of a boat lift, then known as a caisson, designed by Robert Weldon. This plane was short-lived, as it necessitated double trans-shipment of the coal. It was replaced by a flight of locks.

New Moorewood, a Mendip colliery, featured the last mine inclined plane constructed at surface – in 1913. Kilmersdon was the last active plane, closing in 1973.

Stone quarries are represented by sites at Weston-super-Mare and Clevedon. Fullers earth mines near Combe Hay also employed inclined planes. Another possible fullers earth site, with probable plane, lies buried under agricultural land in Englishcombe, near Bath.

Braysdown Colliery, near Radstock
ST 70485547 FOOT – ST 70415573 HEAD

The first incline here connected with the Somerset-shire Coal Canal tramway. A second plane was constructed following the opening of the Somerset & Dorset Railway in 1874. It was twin-track, about 900 feet long with a gradient of 1 in 4.5. The rail gauge was 2 foot 6 inches, apparently relaid to 2 foot from the 1920s. The formation was still extant in 2011.

Camerton New Pit, Camerton
ST 68495809 FOOT – ST 68295823 HEAD

An incline, about 800 feet in length, connected the colliery with Meadgate coal sales depot and functioned from about 1880 to 1950. The rail gauge was possibly 2 foot 4 inches.

Clandown Colliery, Norton Radstock
ST 68285562 FOOT – ST 68105589 HEAD

A branch from the Somersetshire Coal Canal Tramway ran to the colliery, the last section of which was an inclined plane about 900 feet long, with a gradient of 1 in 4. The rail gauge was 3 foot 5½ inches. After the arrival of the Somerset & Dorset, the line was rebuilt as standard gauge in 1882. The incline was at work from 1811 to 1929.

Combe Hay Incline, Somersetshire Coal Canal, Combe Hay
ST 74406038 FOOT – ST 741603 HEAD

A 900-foot-long self-acting plane replaced Robert Weldon's planned caissons and operated from November 1801 to 1805, when it was also abandoned in favour of a flight of 22 conventional locks. Somerset coal had a tendency to break up in trans-shipment on the plane and as a consequence had a reduced sale value. Had the canal been designed as a tub boat waterway rather than employing much larger narrow boats, trans-shipment could have been avoided.[1] The top of the inclined plane, on private land, was partially cleared in the winter of 2010-2011.

The Somerset coalfield, showing the outlying sites with inclined planes. A more detailed map of the Radstock colliery inclines can be seen overleaf.

Combe Hay Fullers Earth Mine, Upper Works, Combe Hay

ST 729612 – UPPER WORKS

Originally established by Samuel Butler of Caisson House, Combe Hay, latterly the mine was operated by the Fullers Earth Union Ltd until April 1968. Mining for Fuller's Earth was undertaken here from the late 19th century and a 2 foot 8 inch gauge system was in use by 1894. The tramway had a cable-worked incline which took the earth up to the works by the Radstock-Bath road. [2]

Conygar Quarry, Clevedon

ST 42207238 FOOT – ST 42307227 HEAD

A narrow-gauge line linked this quarry – via an inclined plane – with a siding on the the Weston, Clevedon and Portishead Light Railway near that line's Walton Park halt. The incline was single track, with a passing loop; possibly three-rail above the loop. It was about 590 feet long with a rise of 58 feet, giving a gradient of a little over 1 in 10. Wagons ran down to the exchange siding under gravity and were hauled back to the quarry by an electric winch. The Weston, Clevedon & Portishead Light Railway opened in 1907 and closed in 1940. Ordnance Survey maps indicate that the quarry system was operational in 1931-32.

Part of the loading ramp, in a deteriorating state, together with a short length of standard gauge rail, survived on private land in 2009. [3]

Inclined planes serving collieries and land sales depots in and around Radstock. These did not all operate concurrently: for instance inclines to the canal tramway at Welton Hill and at Wellsway were later replaced by others to the GWR.

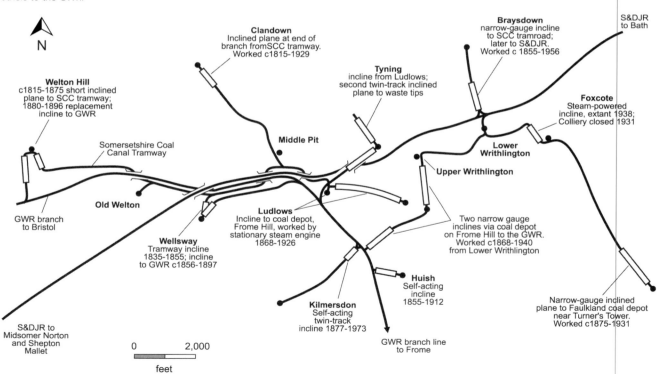

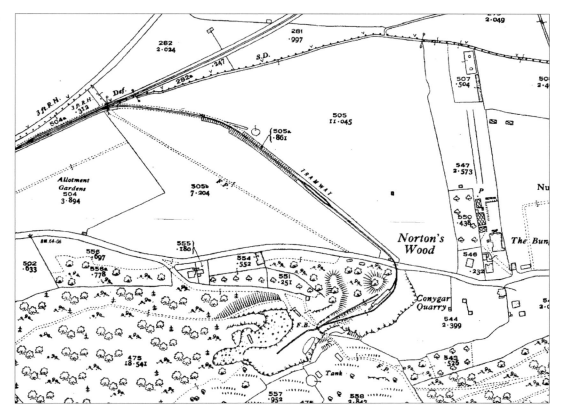

Foxcote Colliery, Hemington

LOWER INCLINE ST 70975534 FOOT – ST 71035518 HEAD
UPPER INCLINE ST 717551 FOOT – ST 718538 HEAD

Coal from Foxcote was sent down to Lower Writhlington by an inclined plane which was constructed by 1866 and was powered by a stationary steam engine. It was single track with a central passing loop, built to the local 2 foot 8½ inch gauge and was about 665 feet long with a gradient of about 1 in 4.5. A second line with the same gauge ran from the colliery up to a coal depot near Turner's Tower and this also required an inclined plane; estimated length 1,260 feet. This line had a passing loop by Castlemead Wood. The two inclines were in operation from about 1866 to 1931 when the pit closed. The engine house for the winding drum on the lower incline has survived and has been converted into a residence.

Greyfield Colliery, High Littleton

ST 640587

At Greyfield, in Clutton parish – since 1956 in High Littleton – a twin-track narrow-gauge tramroad took coal from the mine up to a depot on the Bath-High Littleton road. It was operating in the 1830s but was superseded in 1873 by a siding off the Bristol and North Somerset Railway. The formation now largely survives as a road, known as The Gug.[4]

The summit of the Kilmersdon inclined plane. An NCB employee controlling the brake levers in 1971. *The John Cornwell Collection*

Kilmersdon Colliery, Norton-Radstock
ST 69355424 FOOT – ST 69255415 HEAD

Kilmersdon colliery was worked from 1877 and its twin-track gravity-worked incline was built to standard gauge and descended to the GWR Frome-Radstock branch. It was 480 feet long with a gradient averaging 1 in 4.[6] Secured to a wire cable, one or two 16 ton wagons would be lowered at a time, hauling up an empty one or a couple on the adjoining track. A winding house at the head of the incline contained two horizontal cable drums. The wagons' descent and ascent was managed by the incline operator, who stood at its head, controlling two brake levers bearing on brake bands on the cable drums. It was the last of the Somerset colliery inclines, closing in 1973. The route of this incline still survives between Haydon and Radstock. [7]

Hodshill Fullers Earth Mine, South Stoke
ST 746604 FOOT – ST 746608 HEAD

A short-lived fullers earth mine which was in operation from circa 1886 to 1892. A gravity tramway on a low clay embankment linked the mine with a processing works at Underhill Cottage, to the south, and just east of the flight of locks on the Somersetshire Coal Canal. The mine was owned by W. H. Handley, of Hodhill House, until 1890 when taken over by the Fullers' Earth Union.[5]

Huish Colliery, Kilmersdon
ST 69585404 FOOT – ST 69775408 HEAD

Huish Colliery was at work in 1824. Following the opening of the GWR Frome-Radstock branch, a self-acting incline of 2 foot 8½ inch gauge was constructed in 1855. It linked the pithead with sidings on the branch and up to six tubs each carrying eight hundredweight were let down the 605-foot-long plane at a time. Closure came in 1912. The formation was still extant in 2011.

Lower Conygre Colliery, Timsbury
ST67555787 FOOT, CANAL INCLINE – ST 67355827 HEAD;
ST 67295788 FOOT, INCLINE TO RAILWAY

The first inclined tramway here linked the pithead with the Somersetshire Coal Canal. It was built to the 2 foot 4½ inch gauge, and was self-acting, functioning from 1859. The twin-track plane was about 1,500 feet long. By 1890 the canal had silted up and the incline was used to serve a land sales depot above Weekesley Lane. After 1906 this incline was used as a dirt tip.

A second incline replaced it in 1900 and connected with the GWR's Hallatrow-Limpley Stoke branch line, the successor to the canal. This standard-gauge plane was single track, but with a central passing loop and a three-rail upper section. Both planes ceased work in 1916 when Lower Conygre suffered a major flood. Their formations are still discernible today, although the course of the incline to the canal wharf is partly ploughed out. A footpath passes under the embankment of the second incline, in a tunnel, and is still used.[8]

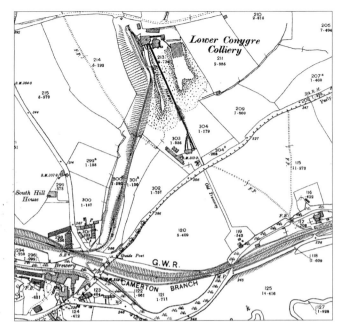

Above: Lower Conygre Colliery, Timsbury, and its two inclines. On the right, the earlier incline to a wharf on the Somerset Coal Canal. On the left, the replacement standard gauge incline to the Camerton branch railway. *Old-Maps*

Right upper: The double-track inclined plane in 1890, now reduced to serving a land sales depot. *Bath in Time - Bath Central Library*

Right lower: The single track replacement incline to the Great Western's Camerton branch line; three rail above the passing loop. *Archive-images*

Lower Writhlington Colliery, Norton-Radstock

ST 69985497 FOOT – ST 70005464 HEAD, FROME HILL
ST 69496426 FOOT – ST 69565441 HEAD, MELLS LANE

A 2 foot 8½ inch tramway linked this coal mine in the Somer valley with the Great Western's branch in the valley below Kilmersdon by way of Frome Hill. It included two inclined planes. The course of the incline running up to Frome Hill was still evident in 1999. Wagons were hauled up a 1 in 5 gradient to a sales depot by Hanover Court powered by a stationary steam engine at the summit. The plane was about 1,080 feet long. The tramway then ran to Mells Lane, where it descended

the second incline to the GWR. This was about 850 feet long and may have been self-acting. Coal was carried over this system from about 1868 to 1940, from Lower Writhlington. [9]

Ludlows Colliery, Norton-Radstock
ST 691548 FOOT – ST 698547 HEAD

A single-track incline worked by a stationary steam engine at its foot took coal up from the colliery pithead to one of two coal depots on Frome Hill. Its length has not been established with any accuracy but is thought to have been about 2,050 feet on a gradient of 1 in 12. It was first operational in 1869. Latterly it was a twin-track plane with rails of 2 foot gauge. It ceased work in 1926, although the colliery closed in 1954.

Milton Quarry, Weston-super-Mare
ST 33706264

Milton Quarry, also known as Butts Quarry, near Weston-super-Mare, was a small limestone working, active early in the twentieth century. It was worked until 1966. At one time it had a cable-worked inclined plane; the rail gauge was 1 foot 11½ inches. It has since been backfilled and now lies under a housing development. [10]

New Moorewood Colliery, Ashwick/Chilcompton
ST 642495 [COLLIERY]
ST 63995004 [DRUM HOUSE, INCLINE HEAD]

This was the last inclined plane to be built on the surface in the Somerset coalfield. It was at work in 1914; coal was hauled out of the valley in which the mine was situated and transported up to the Somerset and Dorset Railway via a 2 foot gauge tramway with an inclined plane at Stock Hill worked by a stationary steam engine at its foot. The incline was about 1,515 feet long with an average gradient of 1 in 7. The trucks were hauled 'main-and-tail', attached to cables wound round drums at the head and foot of the plane.[11] Operations ceased in 1930. The course of the tramway has survived: it was still extant in 2011.

Old Mills and Springfield Collieries, Farington Gurney
ST 65305492 FOOT – ST 65295511

This site originally had a self-acting double-track plane dating from about 1868 which took tubs down from Old Mills to screens at Springfield. It was was replaced by an engine-worked incline with a stationary engine at Old Mills. The new plane also linked the two collieries and was about 610 feet long. Following closure of Old Mills in 1941, the engine and endless rope system were re-sited at Springfield to haul tubs up to the tip by Old Mills. The system was last worked in 1962 and final closure came in 1966. The area has since been levelled but parts of the route to the tip are thought to survive.

Pensford Colliery, Stanton Drew
ST 61856257 FOOT – ST 61836257 HEAD

The 1,150-foot long incline linked the colliery with the Great Western's Bristol-Radstock branch and was completed in 1912. It was designed to be worked by gravity, with one loaded wagon descending, bringing one empty up to the mine. A stationary steam engine was also employed, installed by the summit. Here the empty wagon would be run back into sidings, still attached to the incline rope. Thirty wagons would pass over the incline on a typical working day. Rail gauge was the standard 4 foot 8½ inches. Closure came in 1959; the incline survives as a shallow cutting.

Salisbury Colliery Tramway, Paulton
ST 65895735 FOOT – ST 65765706 HEAD

A tramroad climbed south from Paulton Basin on the Somersetshire Coal Canal to provide access to coal pits at Brittens, Littlebrook, Paulton Ham, Paulton Hill, and Simons Hill, with a terminus at Salisbury Colliery. The line was laid as a plateway, with stone sleeper blocks. There appear to have been two inclined planes: the first was of twin-track formation and lay immediately to the south of Paulton Foundry, near the canal basin, and served all the above collieries. It probably functioned from 1815. A second plane may have existed on the branch serving Simons Hill pit (at ST 658562), which closed circa 1844. These inclines were probably worked by gravity; the coal pits closed relatively early and so details are not forthcoming.

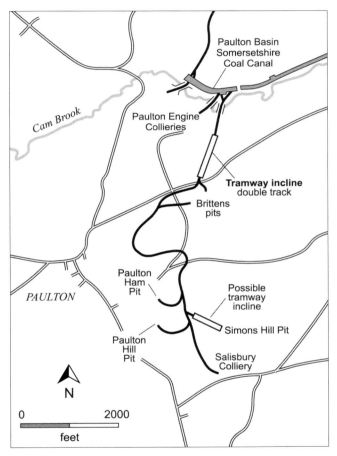

The tramway from Paulton Basin on the Somersetshire Coal Canal to Salisbury Colliery required a gravity-worked incline. It is thought a second incline was necessary to lower coal from the Simons Hill pit. The route had closed by 1871 and the rails had been lifted by 1886.

Tyning Colliery, Norton-Radstock
ST 69295498 FOOT – ST 69605514 HEAD

The tramways and railways here are a little more complex than elsewhere. A tramway was built at some time after 1838 to take colliery waste to a tip by Tyning. With the arrival of the Great Western's broad gauge branch from Frome in 1857, a siding, partly on incline, was laid alongside the narrow-gauge tramway to the colliery. This link was converted to standard gauge in the 1870s and survived until 1909 when the pit closed. The incline was about 1,100 feet long and was worked by a stationary steam engine. Both railways were carried over the Somerset & Dorset Railway on a bridge, following its arrival at Radstock in 1874. The bridge was demolished in 1960. The standard gauge incline was single track at its foot, with a passing loop and a three-rail upper section. The tramway served to take waste from Middle pit and from Ludlows and was extended to the north west of Tyning colliery by 1898. Operations ceased with the closure of Ludlows in 1954.

Vobster Colliery, Vobster, Mells
ST 70584911 FOOT – ST 70834942 HEAD

At Vobster, in the Mells River valley, a steam-powered plane was necessary to link the tramway that connected Breach and Vobster Collieries with the Newbury railway. It was in operation from 1860 to 1878. The plane ran to the south east of the Vobster Inn, climbed past Tor Rock on its western side and then crossed the line of the abandoned Dorset & Somerset Canal as it reached its summit.[12] The formation survives as a footpath, partly in cutting with a stone revetment.

Wellsway Colliery, Norton-Radstock
ST 68035476 TRAMWAY FOOT – ST 68015455 HEAD

A tramway here linked the pit with the Somersetshire Coal Canal Tramway, in the Somer valley to the north, from circa 1835. Its total length was 920 feet; part of that, perhaps 690 feet, was on an inclined plane, probably self-acting, with a gradient of about 1 in 8. It bridged the river Somer at ST 681548. The rail gauge was probably 3 foot 5½ inches.

This was replaced in 1873 or so by a standard-gauge siding from the Bristol and North Somerset Railway; later the Great Western's Bristol-Radstock branch. It ran in from the east, with a twin-track inclined plane at its upper end, on the approach to the pithead and screens. After 1897 coal was taken underground to Ludlows pit and the second incline became redundant. The second plane was about 900 feet long on a gradient of 1 in 9.

Stone sleeper blocks, remnants of the earlier plane, were still to be seen in situ in 1969 in a wood between the A362 and A367 roads. The foot of the second incline has been lost under the more recent Radstock-Midsomer Norton road, but part survives as a lane.[13]

Welton Hill Colliery, Norton-Radstock

OLD INCLINE ST 66705508 FOOT – ST 66665519 HEAD
NEW INCLINE ST 66585484 FOOT – ST 66585518 HEAD

Welton Hill was served by two inclines. The earlier formation linked the pit with the Welton tramway, an extension of the Somersetshire Coal Canal Tramway, as early as 1815, when the pit was at work. The rail gauge was thought to be 3 foot 5½ inches. This route incorporated a 500-foot-long self-acting twin-track incline. This was replaced in 1880 by a second route situated to the west, with a 950-foot-long self-acting single-track plane, also narrow gauge – but the gauge is not known – linking the colliery with screens and sidings on the Great Western's Bristol-Radstock branch line. It had a short life; the colliery closed in 1896.

Withy Mills Colliery, Timsbury

ST 66375775 FOOT – ST 66275789 HEAD

An incline plane linking the colliery with the Somersetshire Coal Canal – where there was a wharf – was established at an early date, when the colliery opened – circa 1815. It was a twin-track formation, worked by gravity. 'L' tramplates rather than rails were utilised, laid on stone sleeper blocks. The plane was about 660 feet long with a rise of 72 feet, giving a gradient of 1 in 9. Closure came in the 1870s. The colliery site has been cleared; the route of the incline survives just east of the linear spoil heap but is inaccessible.

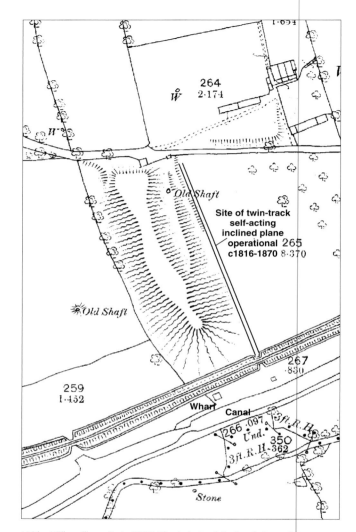

Withy Mills colliery site in 1886. The twin-track inclined plane plateway ran down the east side of the spoil heap from the colliery to a wharf on the Somersetshire Coal Canal. The GWR branch railway at the foot of the spoil tip came after closure of the colliery and canal, in 1882. *Old-Maps*

Somerset: the Mendips to the Blackdowns

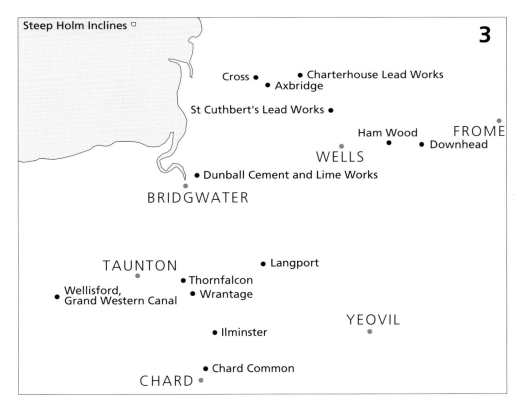

Steep Holm Inclines

3

Cross •

• Charterhouse Lead Works

• Axbridge

St Cuthbert's Lead Works •

Ham Wood

FROME

• Downhead

WELLS

• Dunball Cement and Lime Works

BRIDGWATER

TAUNTON

• Langport

• Thornfalcon

Wellisford,
Grand Western Canal

• Wrantage

YEOVIL

• Ilminster

• Chard Common

CHARD •

Southern Mendip includes stone quarries, an ochre mine and lead mines all employing inclined planes. In the Bristol Channel, military engineers constructed a series of narrow gauge inclined planes on Steep Holm during World War II. In the south of the county the sites of five planes survive that once served the Grand Western Canal and the Chard Canal.

Three of these canal inclines were originally planned by James Green, following his success with the Bude and Rolle Canals in Cornwall and Devon.

For Mendip collieries please see the North and North-east Somerset section.

Surviving balance wheel at Axbridge Hill. *Michael Messenger*

Axbridge Hill Iron Ochre Mine, Axbridge
ST 43155510

Above Axbridge village an opencast mine, now heavily overgrown, was worked for iron ochre in the 1920s. To its south a short inclined plane ran down the Mendip edge on twin 50cm gauge 'Decauville' track. The balance wheel at the head of the plane was still extant in 2008, cast by ironfounders Dening & Co of Chard.[1]

Chard Canal, Chard Common Incline, Chard
ST 33911049 FOOT – ST 33731027 HEAD

Length	1,032 feet
Rise	86 feet
Gradient	1 in 12
Site today	course well preserved, eroded at foot

Ilminster Incline, Ilminster
ST 35651418 FOOT – ST 35691406 HEAD (ESTIMATED)

Length	492 feet
Rise	82 feet
Gradient	1 in 6
Site today	course well preserved

Wrantage Incline, North Curry
ST 310221

Length	165 feet
Rise	27 feet
Gradient	1 in 6
Site today	well preserved except at summit

Thornfalcon Incline, Thornfalcon
ST 284241

Length	165 feet
Rise	28 feet
Gradient	1 in 6
Site today	in cutting, partly infilled by tipping

In 1830 James Green planned the route from Creech St Michael – on the Bridgwater and Taunton Canal – to Chard. The canal was to have a rise of 231 feet in 13½ miles. Designed for 26-foot long tub boats, it was to have two lifts, two inclined planes and three tunnels.[2]

Work started in 1835. Green was removed shortly afterwards and Sir William Cubitt, the contractor, saw the enterprise through to completion. Sydney Hall, the engineer who had been recommended by Cubitt in 1834, dispensed with lifts at Wrantage and Thornfalcon and substituted short inclined planes at these locations. All the planes were worked by waterpower, using overshot wheels, and were twin track, except for the 1,032 feet long Chard Common incline, which was single track with a rise of 86 feet and was powered by a patent Whitelaw and Stirrat water turbine installed at the foot. The turbine worked on a head of 25 feet with a water flow of 725 cubic feet per minute. The 50-acre Chard Reservoir was constructed to provide water for the turbine; it in turn was fed by a two-mile-long leat from the river Isle.

It appears that cradles were employed on these planes. The canal opened throughout in May 1842,[3] by which time it was outdated – the railway age had arrived. In 1855 the main freight was from south Wales; over 14,900 tons of coal, culm and coke, but trade was already little more than 60% of that in 1845 and far less than originally forecast. This meant the initial debt could never be fully serviced. The canal closed in 1866.[4]

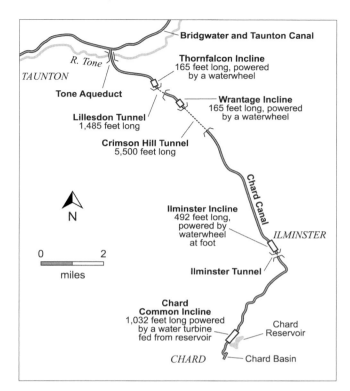

Chard Canal. The inclines at Thornfalcon and Wrantage were originally designed as lifts. The canal had a total rise of 231 feet and its route was 13½ miles long. It opened in 1842 and closed in 1866, to be replaced by a GWR branch line.

A section of the 50-acre Chard Reservoir, Chard Canal. It was formed to provide the power for an early water turbine on the Chard Common Incline and was fed by a two-mile long leat from the river Isle at Nimmer.

Charterhouse Lead Works, Blackmoor Bottom, Priddy
ST 506560

A tramway incline was constructed in 1849-50 to raise lead slimes from earlier mining on the 'Ubley Grounds', for dressing, prior to smelting. This incline was worked by an eight-horse-power steam engine at its head, where a reverbatory furnace was set up to smelt the slimes and slags. The steam engine powered winding drums; haulage was by chains. It also powered a second incline. The aim had been to recover twenty tons of lead a month. The endeavour had closed by the 1880s.[5]

Cross Quarry, near Axbridge
ST 41405477 FOOT – ST 41405489 HEAD

Limestone has long been quarried on Mendip and supports a major industry today at Whatley. Many smaller quarries have been worked and are now closed: a few required inclined planes. A small quarry at Cross, near Axbridge, incorporated a limekiln which stood by the head of a gravity-worked inclined plane about 540 feet long. This dropped 75 feet to the road from Axbridge to Compton Bishop. It was extant in 1930.[6]

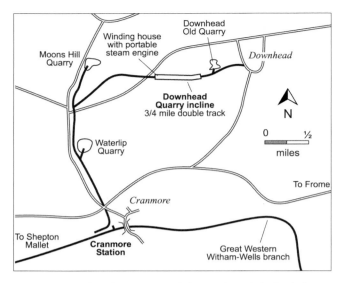

A tramway – with a three-quarter-mile-long twin-track inclined plane – from Downhead Quarry to the Great Western branch line at Cranmore. It also served two other quarries. The narrow-gauge route was also known as the Tadhill Mineral Railway and was worked by locomotives between the incline head and Cranmore Station.

Downhead Quarry Tramway, Downhead
ST 68154589 FOOT – ST 67404586 HEAD

At Downhead andesite, a volcanic rock similar to basalt, was quarried for roadstone from about 1905. The quarry was connected to the Great Western's Cranmore station via a 2-foot gauge tramway. In 1907 a three-quarter mile incline was constructed down to the quarry; it was twin track and worked by a Brown & May stationary steam engine until about 1925.[7]

Dunball Portland Cement and Blue Lias Lime Works, Puriton
ST 31494111

The construction of the Bristol & Exeter Railway through the Polden Hills in the late 1830s led to quarrying by John Board and other companies with access to the main line, and the development of wharves at Dunball. By the early twentieth century a system of 2-foot tramways served the complex.

A single-track inclined plane linked the higher and lower levels of this extensive works and can be seen in a rather fuzzy photograph taken in 1928 and was shown on the Ordnance Survey 1:2,500 map of 1930.

The system closed and track was lifted in 1954. The whole site was bulldozed in the 1970s during construction of the M5 Motorway, which enters a cutting at Junction 23. The incline was just to the south of the interchange.[8]

Grand Western Canal
Wellisford inclined plane, Wellington Without
ST 10212161 FOOT – ST 10102165 HEAD

James Green planned an extension to the Grand Western Canal in 1830. The canal was to have linked Taunton and Topsham, but the war with France and other matters forced abandonment of the scheme. Green's project, to link Taunton and Canonsleigh, on the branch to Tiverton, involved seven lifts and an inclined plane at Wellisford. The plane, 440 feet long and with a rise of 81 feet and a gradient of 1 in 5½, turned out to be Green's nemesis as a canal engineer. It was to have the bucket-in-a-well system that he had used with relative success at the Hobbacott incline on the Bude Canal.

Green miscalculated the power needed. At the twin-track Wellisford plane boats were to be carried on wheeled cradles rather than relying on integral wheels. As on the Bude inclines, a short reverse incline was necessary at the summit to confine the canal at the upper level. The plane was so arranged that the descending tub boat was pulled over the apex of the two inclines at the summit as the ascending boat was readied at the foot of the climb. Once the upper boat began its descent, its weight added gravity to the powered machinery bringing up the lower boat. Power was provided by buckets filled with about 10 tons of water in an 80-foot shaft at the incline summit. This was insufficient to raise an empty boat and cradle from the upper canal to the head of the main incline. A bucket holding 25 tons of water would have been required to lift a loaded boat of 8 tons. The 935-foot Hobbacott plane used buckets with 15 tons of water, but cradles were not used there and the boats, loaded, weighed only 6 tons. In the event a 12 horse-power stationary steam engine was installed by the incline summit and the canal was eventually fully opened in June 1838. The steam-powered incline and counter-balanced

lifts remained in use until 1867; the canal was not a financial success. Nevertheless Green's lifts were the first successful application of canal lift technology in Britain.

His miscalculations at Wellisford led to Green's removal as engineer from this and the Chard canal. At the same time cost overruns resulted in his dismissal from two further projects in south Wales.[9]

The incline is on private land.

Ham Wood Quarry incline, Shepton Mallet
ST 61064528 FOOT – ST 61254520 HEAD

The Somerset & Dorset Railway's extension to Bath, which opened in 1874, encouraged the development of quarries at Ham Wood, Croscombe and nearby at Windsor Hill. Ham Wood was linked to sidings by the main line by a twin-track 2-foot gauge tramway with an inclined plane. It was active in 1903,[10] and was probably powered by a stationary engine.

Grand Western Canal. The Wellisford inclined plane in 1994.

The eastern section of the Grand Western Canal, showing the location of the inclined plane and the various canal lifts.

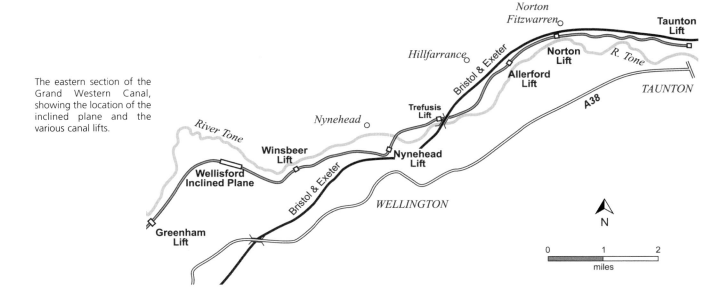

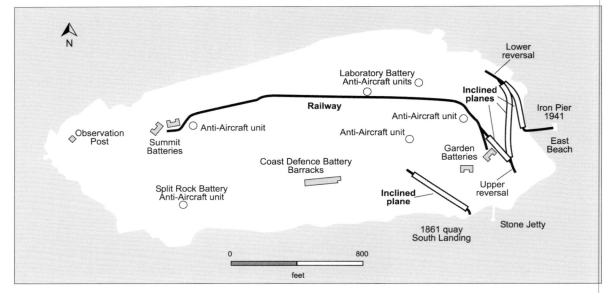

Steep Holm Island, Bristol Channel. Three inclined planes, built in 1941, rose from East Beach. These served anti-aircraft batteries and 6-inch guns guarding shipping in the Bristol Channel. A plane, built in 1866, rose from the South Landing and also served the military. All the planes are now footpaths, giving access to the island's plateau.

Right: the upper reversal in 2010; the inclines now serve as footpaths. *Chris Allen*
Below: The three 1941 inclines visible from the landing beach. *www.Willys-MB.*

Military railways, Steep Holm Island, Bristol Channel

WORLD WAR II INCLINED PLANES:
ST 232606 FOOT – ST 231606 HEAD, THIRD INCLINE
VICTORIAN INCLINED PLANE:
ST 231605 FOOT – ST 230606 HEAD

Steep Holm, an island in the Bristol Channel, was part of the defences developed by Lord Palmerston when France appeared to threaten. Several gun batteries and a barracks block were constructed between 1865 and 1869. Works constructed in 1866 included an inclined plane that ran up the cliff from a limekiln by a quay built on the south of the island to the plateau. It was 350 feet long and had a manual winch at the incline head. The rails had been lifted by 1883.

The Second World War led to further defences here. A 600mm gauge railway was constructed by the Royal Engineers in 1941 from a new jetty at East Beach to the island's plateau, 256 feet above sea level. The rails, with integral metal sleepers, were re-used from captured German 'Feldbahn' or field railways, taken in World War I and subsequently stored at Longmoor and Rochester.

Three inclined planes, forming a zig-zag route with reversals, were necessary to reach the summit level. They were each cable-operated and single track with gradients of 1 in 2 or 1 in 3; trucks with a capacity of 406 kilos were hauled up by diesel-powered winches, possibly just one at a time. The inclines were used to bring in supplies of materials for the construction of new batteries and later for supplies of ammunition. The Victorian incline from the South Landing was rehabilitated at this time; it too was equipped with 600mm track. On the plateau, above the zig-zag inclines, the railway from East Beach employed mules to haul wagons to the Summit Batteries sited to the west of the island.

The East Beach jetty was demolished in 1946 and the railway was rendered redundant. The concrete winch houses are now ruinous but rails remain underfoot on the inclines, now serving as a path to the island's plateau. [11]

Parrett Navigation Incline, Langport
ST 412262

A short incline linked a wharf on the Parrett Navigation with the Great Western Railway at Langport. It was in use from 1853 to circa 1872 and was worked by a horse whim at the incline head. [12]

St Cuthbert's Lead Works, Priddy
ST 544505

Intermittently, at least from the 1860s to closure in 1908, the St Cuthbert's Lead Works at Priddy worked old mine dumps, re-smelting the ores. A twin-track inclined plane tramway, running west-east, is shown on the Ordnance Survey 25-inch map of 1903. It linked a ravine containing debris from earlier mining with the works and was constructed at some time after 1886. This feature was extant in 1947 when the RAF took vertical aerials of the site, by which time the lead works were ruinous. [13]

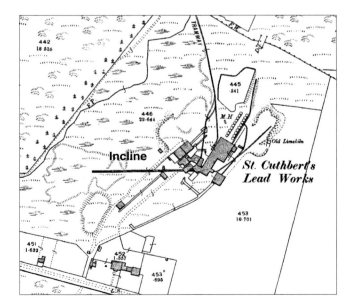

Incline at St Cuthbert's Lead Works, Priddy. *Old-Maps*

Dorset and East Devon

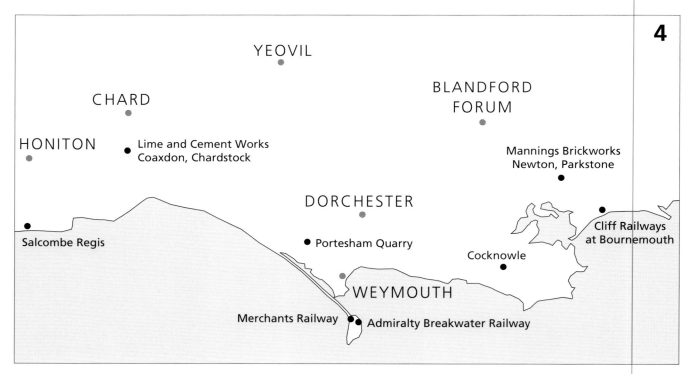

4

YEOVIL

CHARD

BLANDFORD FORUM

HONITON

Lime and Cement Works
Coaxdon, Chardstock

Mannings Brickworks
Newton, Parkstone

DORCHESTER

Cliff Railways
at Bournemouth

Salcombe Regis

Portesham Quarry

Cocknowle

WEYMOUTH

Merchants Railway

Admiralty Breakwater Railway

In Dorset Portland stone quarries were early users of inclines. At Portland there were several inclined planes at work in the nineteenth century. The main incline of the Merchants Railway operated for over a century; the Admiralty incline, at 4,500 feet, was one of the longest in the south west.

The twentieth century witnessed the construction of three cliff railways at Bournemouth. These operate today.

The limestone quarry and kilns at Chardstock in east Devon are recorded here. A little further west, near Sidmouth, an early twentieth-century inclined plane survives as a footpath. Other minor narrow-gauge single track inclines were once to be found at the Gillingham Brick & Tile Works and at Norden Clay Works near Corfe Castle.

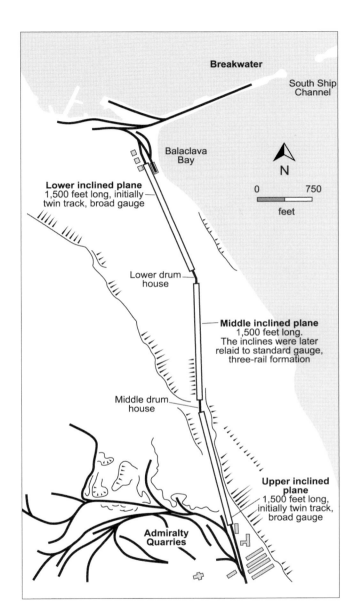

Breakwater

South Ship
Channel

Balaclava
Bay

N

0   750

feet

Lower inclined plane
1,500 feet long, initially
twin track, broad gauge

Lower drum
house

Middle inclined plane
1,500 feet long.
The inclines were later
relaid to standard gauge,
three-rail formation

Middle drum
house

**Upper inclined
plane**
1,500 feet long,
initially twin track,
broad gauge

**Admiralty
Quarries**

Admiralty Breakwater Railway, Isle of Portland

INCLINE HEAD	SY 70007280
HIGHER DRUM	SY69997280
MIDDLE DRUM	SY 69897322
LOWER DRUM	SY 69897363
INCLINE FOOT	SY 697740

The Admiralty incline was established in 1849 for the construction of Portland Breakwater. It was built to the 7-foot broad gauge with a gradient varying from 1 in 10 to 1 in 15. Stone was taken from quarries high up on the island, worked by convicts. The plane was divided into three sections with Higher, Middle and Lower winding drums. Each section was 1,500 foot long and initially the route was laid as double track. The incline head was by HM Prison, where there was a weighbridge. Here tramways branched off to the north west where stone was quarried by prisoners working in Admiralty Quarries and Withies Croft Quarries. They were supervised by warders in lookout posts.

Charles Dickens described the incline working in 1858:
'Up the hill to the right ran the inclines; the heavy four wagon trains rattle down them .. each wagon averages 12 tons in weight ..' Almost six million tons of stone were carried down the Breakwater incline until completion of the project in 1872. By 1889 the incline was mapped as 'old railway' but was subsequently relaid to standard gauge to serve new quarry workings. The route was still in use in 1921, laid in three-rail configuration with passing loops below each drum house. By 1938 all the Admiralty incline track and associated tramways in the quarries had been lifted.[1]

The Admiralty Incline, Portland. The route was formed from a series of three broad-gauge inclines, each with its own drum house and operated from 1849. The breakwater was completed in 1872 and for a while the route was disused. By 1921 the railway had been re-configured as three-rail standard gauge. A series of quarries were served by sidings to the west of the upper incline's summit.

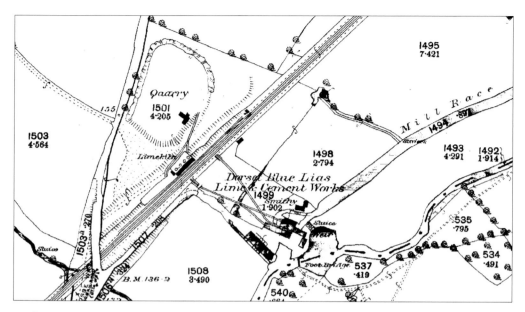

Dorset Blue Lime and Cement Works, Coaxdon, Chardstock. Plan in 1890; by 1905 the track layout had been simplified. The quarry, inclined plane and kiln bank lay to the north of the London & South Western Railway. To the south, the mill leat from the river Axe powered the incline, turning the waterwheel in Coaxdon Mill. *Old-Maps*

Cocknowle, Church Knowle, near Corfe Castle

SY 93238210 [SUMMIT]
SY 93218221 [FOOT, NORTH]
SY 93258202 [FOOT, SOUTH, 1889]

There was no road over Knowle Hill in the mid nineteenth century. A tramway, operational in 1875, crossed Knowle Hill to reach marl pits on its south side at Cocknowle. In 1881 it was reported that *'marl is lowered by means of a double action drum, saving many miles of cartage by way of Corfe Castle'.*[2]

In 1889 the route ran due north-south; there was a passing loop at the summit. Kidner described the northern section as a balanced worked incline, but in practice the whole system must have been worked this way.

The northern section appears to have been three rail, about 330 feet long with a rise of 125 feet. The track to the south of the summit may only have been single track and was about 210 feet long with a rise of 75 feet. At the northern terminus the marl was loaded into carts and hauled to Ridge, near Wareham, for processing by the Wareham Cement Company. By 1901 the southern track had been lifted and a new, much

longer, tramway ran almost eastwards along the ridge into extended quarry workings. It is not clear how the northern incline was worked in this later phase. A passing loop was still extant at the summit of the tramway. By 1928 all track had been lifted and the quarries were disused.[3]

Dorset Blue Lime and Cement Works, Coaxdon, Chardstock

ST 31080055

The London & South Western Railway extended to Exeter in 1860. At Coaxdon William Wheaton was working a quarry to the north of the line for the production of lime and cement. A bank of four kilns was established by a siding alongside the railway. A cable-operated inclined plane brought limestone up from the quarry to the kiln bank. It was part of a narrow gauge system, and single track. Derrick Warren remembers seeing the system at work, as a boy in the 1930s. He recalls power was supplied by a waterwheel in the redundant Coaxdon Mill, which stood south of the railway, on a leat from the river Axe. The mill building contained the brake drum and the brakesman's cabin. The precise details of the operation are not known: how power was transmitted to the incline on the far side of the railway, nor how the communications system, using semaphore signals, worked.

In the late nineteenth century the company was known as Dorset Lime Cement and Stone Co, and then as the Dorset Blue Lias Lime and Cement Works. The works operated under the Exeter Brick and Tile Co from 1914 to 1925, and was still active in 1933. Vegetation has now obscured the line of the incline; the quarry is now a fishing lake.[4]

East Cliff and West Cliff Railways, Bournemouth

East Cliff: SZ 096909
West Cliff: SZ 085906

The East Cliff and West Cliff Railways at Bournemouth were both opened in 1908. Built for the Bournemouth Corporation, the cable inclines were powered by electric motors from the outset. Both planes are twin track, the rails set at 5 foot 6 inch gauge and are 170 feet and 145 feet long respectively. Wooden-bodied cars were replaced in the 1960s with aluminium vehicles carrying 12 passengers. The East Cliff line has a gradient of 1:1.45; at West Cliff it is 1:1.42. On the East Cliff, power is provided by a 25 horse-power motor working off a three-phase 415v supply and at West Cliff the motor is rated at 28 horse-power. The supply was originally 500v DC, converted from mains electricity. Civil engineering improvements have included cliff stabilisation either side of the lines and the provision of new entrance lobbies at the head and foot of the cliffs.

Fisherman's Walk Railway, Boscombe, Bournemouth

SZ 130913

A third funicular was constructed at Fisherman's Walk and opened in 1935. It was built to a gauge of 5 foot 8 inches, again with twin tracks and was initially powered by a 21-horse-power 500 DC motor. It has a gradient of 1:1.49 and is 128 feet long. The three Bournemouth railways operate in spring, summer and autumn months, usually from April until October. The lines are owned and operated by Bournemouth Borough Council.[5]

East Cliff Railway, Bournemouth. *Richard and Gill Long*

West Cliff Railway, Bournemouth.
Chris Downer, under a Creative Commons License

Mannings Brickworks, Newton, Parkstone

SZ 037945

A 2-foot gauge tramway which included an incline, possibly two, served the works to the west of Alderney Hospital. This was heathland between the wars. Mannings Brickworks was extant in 1924 and by 1933 tramways were laid into claypits here and at Alderney Works; the latter had a double-track line leading into its pit which may also have been worked as an inclined plane. These inclines appear to have been powered by stationary engines: Mannings Brickworks had one sited by the head of its tramways. The site was known as Omnium Factory (Brickworks) by 1953 and a single tramway remained. It is now within a built-up area.[6]

Merchants Railway, Isle of Portland

SY 68607432 FOOT OF MAIN INCLINE
SY 68887378 HEAD OF INCLINE
SY 69357335 EAST VERNE INCLINE
SY 69287322 VERNE INCLINE TO WAYCROFT QUARRIES

Also known as the Portland Railway. An Act of Parliament in 1825 authorised construction of the railway to carry dimension stone from quarries on the island down to Castletown Pier in Portland harbour. The line was built to the 4 foot 6 inch gauge. Haulage was by horses: wagons were taken from Priory Corner, on the island's plateau, around a contour route to the incline head. The incline was built in two sections, each with its own winding drum at the head. The upper section was 910 feet long and the lower section 846 feet. There was a short level section between the two where there was a passing loop. The whole incline route was otherwise laid with a common centre rail. It was worked entirely on the counter-balance principle. There were numerous tramway branches into quarries: at Waycroft, King Barrow, Tout, Immosthay and others. Additional short inclines were adopted to link some of these quarries with the Merchants Railway.

Chains were used to lower loaded wagons down the inclines and haul empties up. But these broke on occasion and caused damage. Steel cables were proposed in 1857 but not installed.

The Merchants Railway in use. Dimension stone being lowered on the three-rail section. *Archive-images*

The Merchants Railway: foot of incline, from an old coloured postcard. *Isle of Portland Heritage Trust*

By 1863 the two inclines were merged into one and steel ropes had been introduced. The route was now reconfigured as one incline, worked with a single brake drum. The wire rope lasted between four and seven years before requiring replacement: it was typically three-and-one-eighth-inch thick.

By 1861 the railway had been extended up a second incline to the East Drum, East Verne, but the head of this route was lost in 1866 when the Verne fort was built on the site. It was replaced by a third incline into the Waycroft Quarries, which ascended from Tillycombe. This was constructed in about 1870.

A semaphore signal was installed at the foot of the main plane in 1876 as a means of communication with the incline keepers at the summit. New brake gear was introduced on this incline in 1885 and again in 1904, such that wagons could be brought to a halt on it. The Portland Railway Company operated the inclined plane from 1826 to 1939, possibly the longest period an incline was in use in the south west. In 114 years of operation the incline had transported 4,561,796 tons of stone to Portland harbour for shipment.[7]

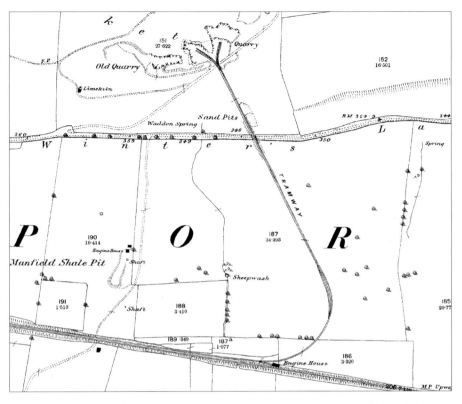

The incline to the Portesham Quarry, also known as Rocket Quarry, connected with the GWR's Abbotsbury branch line. From the Ordnance Survey 1: 2,500 map 1888. *Old-Maps*

Portesham Quarry, Portesham, near Abbotsbury
SY 61488545 FOOT – SY 611859 HEAD

The Portland limestone quarry at Portesham was connected by rail with the Great Western's Abbotsbury branch line at Portesham Station. George Barclay Bruce constructed the tramway, which included a three-rail standard-gauge incline, with a passing loop, in 1885. It was 1,530 feet long with a rise of 250 feet. It was very probably self acting. The works were leased to Sir George Eliot in 1887 but the incline was disused by 1901.[8]

Salcombe Hill, Salcombe Regis, near Sidmouth
SY 139882

Sir Norman Lockyer had an observatory and planetarium built on Salcombe Hill in 1912; it has since been named after him. He also had South Down built as his retirement home, some way down the hill. Stone for its construction was taken down from the highway by the observatory on a funicular railway. Its course now appears to be a public footpath.

Exmoor, North Devon and Lundy

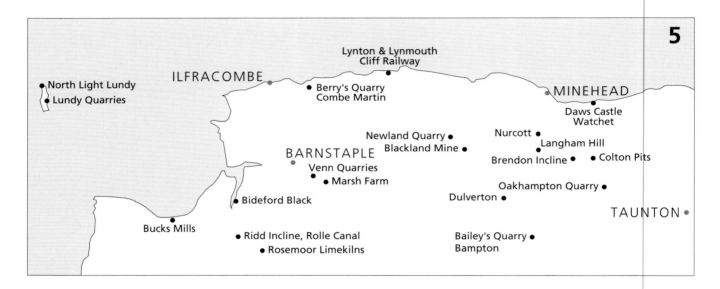

5

North Light Lundy
Lundy Quarries

ILFRACOMBE

Lynton & Lynmouth
Cliff Railway

Berry's Quarry
Combe Martin

MINEHEAD

Daws Castle
Watchet

Newland Quarry
Blackland Mine

Nurcott
Langham Hill

BARNSTAPLE

Venn Quarries
Marsh Farm

Brendon Incline
Colton Pits

Oakhampton Quarry

Dulverton

TAUNTON

Bideford Black

Bucks Mills

Ridd Incline, Rolle Canal
Rosemoor Limekilns

Bailey's Quarry
Bampton

Brendon incline, which linked mines on the Brendon Hills with the port of Watchet, and the smelters at Ebbw Vale, is by far the most impressive surviving monument to nineteenth-century engineering in the Exmoor National Park. Had it survived in its entirety, the Ridd incline plane on the Rolle Canal, would also have qualified as a significant major structure.

This section includes west Somerset. It also includes a diversity of planes: inclines for mines, quarries, limekilns and a lighthouse. Here too is one of the earliest cliff railways, linking Lynton with Lynmouth, and still in operation.

The remains of four further inclines are to be found on the island of Lundy.

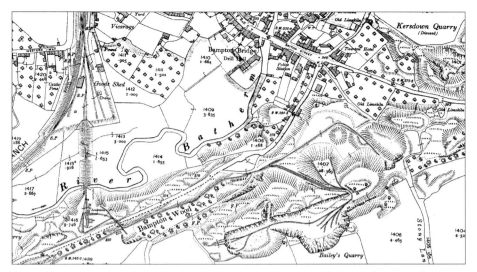
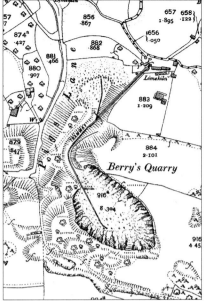

Bailey's Quarry, Bampton, 1904. The inclined plane can be seen as the double-track section of tramway running SE-NW, lower centre right. *Old-Maps*
Right: Berry's Quarry, Combe Martin, 1904, with the tramway incline running down to the limekiln. *Old-Maps*

Bailey's Quarry, Bampton
SS 95982189 FOOT – SS 96072185 HEAD

A narrow gauge twin-track incline, almost certainly self acting, took stone down from the quarry to a line which ran through Bampton Wood, above the Tiverton road, to limekilns to the south of the river Batherm. These were connected via a standard gauge siding – which bridged the River Batherm – to the GWR's Exe Valley branch line south of Bampton station. The incline was operational in 1907; it was about 500 feet long with a rise of 80 feet, giving a gradient of 1 in 6¼. The upper site is now rather overgrown. Housing has now been built on part of the lower quarry site.[1]

Berry's Quarry, Combe Martin
SS 59284578 foot – SS 59204570 head

A double-track self-acting incline led down from the limestone quarry to a limekiln by the river Umber. The 3-foot gauge incline was active from 1900 to 1915 and briefly from the autumn of 1927 until the spring of 1928. It was about 320 feet long with a rise of 62 feet. Re-cycled bridge rail was used on the chain-hauled plane. Lime was carted as far away as Simonsbath.[2]

Bideford Black Culm Mine, East-the-Water, Bideford
SS 471263

In the mid-nineteenth century culm was mined on the hill above East-the-Water. The 'Great Anthracite Bed' was mined for culm, or slack, while the smaller 'Paint Seam' was worked for black pigments used in the production of paints. An incline worked by a steam engine lowered wagons of 'black' from the top of Mines Road, near the mine's adit, to a point east of Grange Road, where the tramway ran on trestle over Barnstaple Street to a wharf on the river Torridge. Pollution from coal dust led to closure of the incline, and the trestle – which can be seen in a hazy photograph of circa 1862 – was dismantled in 1865. The mine continued to be worked for pigments and later included an inclined shaft, powered by an electric winch. The tramway route was built over by the 1880s.[3]

The Brendon Hill incline in 1863. The track layout at its foot was simplified in later years. *M.H. Jones Collection*

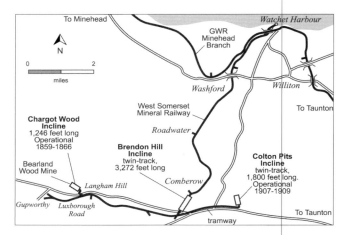

The route of the West Somerset Mineral Railway linking mines on the Brendons with the port at Watchet – and so to smelters in south Wales – via the major incline at Brendon Hill. There were also secondary inclines at Langham Hill, and later at Colton Pits, down to iron ore mine adits.

Halfway up the incline. Seen in March 2009. The 1 in 4 gradient was maintained throughout by the construction of four embankments and five cuttings. *Richard Cutts*

Blackland Mine, Withypool and Hawkridge

SS 84173690 FOOT – SS 84503703 HEAD

Blackland iron mine, on Exmoor, was a short-lived venture. It was worked from 1875-1876 and from 1908-1910. In 1908 the Somerset Mineral Syndicate re-used a 1,250-foot long incline from the Pennycombe Water up to the Withypool road to take ores mined and stockpiled in the nineteenth century phase: the ores here contained sulphides which rendered them valueless unless calcined prior to smelting. The narrow-gauge inclined plane was powered by a stationary engine at its head. Its steepest section survives as a stone platform.[4]

Brendon Incline,
West Somerset Mineral Railway, Old Cleeve

ST 029352 FOOT, COMBEROW – ST 02333446 HEAD, BRENDON HILL

On the edge of the Brendon Hills, the incline at Comberow was the outstanding feature of the West Somerset Mineral Railway, constructed to take iron ore from local mines to the port of Watchet and so via Newport to smelters at Ebbw Vale in south Wales. The line was the brainchild of the ambitious ironmaster Thomas Brown (1803-1884) who was the managing partner of the Ebbw Vale Company in 1853. It was designed by Rice Hopkins (1807-1857) who died before the route was completed. Construction of the incline took four years and involved four embankments – one of them major – and five cuttings. The two 18-foot diameter winding drums were installed on a single axle, beneath the track, at the summit, at Brendon Hill, in 1861. The line opened in that year.

The twin-track 3,272-foot long plane lowered standard-gauge wagons 770 feet on a uniform 1 in 4 gradient from the Brendon plateau to the valley below. Twelve minutes were needed to lower a single wagon containing five tons of ore.

The brakesman at the summit, at Brendon Hill, operated a signal at the foot of the incline, at Comberow, where the banksman was based. He in turn operated a second semaphore signal at Brendon Hill, to signal to the brakesman and his crew. At Comberow the ascending wagon was attached to the incline cable by three short chains. The banksman here would then pull off the signal half a mile away at the top of the bank. Here the descending wagon, loaded with ore, was attached to its cable and the signal at Comberow would be pulled off and the stop block at the head of the incline cleared. The brake on the winding drum would be released and a timber bar used to lever the wagon onto the plane. The weight of the loaded wagon would draw up the ascending one. Braking was necessary as this wagon came over the head of the plane.

At the time the incline was built, the smelters it served were already in decline. The impressively engineered incline was part of an endeavour which was not really commercially viable. Ores were taken by train to Watchet where they were shipped to Newport and thence by rail again to smelters at Ebbw Vale and Abersychan. By 1882 Spanish ores were undercutting the market and the Brendon mines closed in 1883: as it was they had failed to deliver the volume of ores anticipated and the incline was probably never operated to its capacity. A second-hand Robey steam-engine was installed to power the drums at closure of the mines, so that goods could be hauled up to Brendon Hill. In the 1890s the track layout at the foot of the incline was simplified. The line continued in use until 1898. It was resurrected briefly in the years 1907-1910 when the incline reverted to gravity operation.[5]

The incline site is now owned by Exmoor National Park and is worth exploration, although access is not possible at the foot. It is listed Grade II by English Heritage.

Bucks Mills. The eastern limekiln perched on a cliff with incline to the platform, powered by a horse gin, to the left. Seen in 1956. The plane was worked from 1780 to 1870. *B. D. Hughes Collection*

Bucks Mills, Woolfardisworthy

SS 35482366

At Bucks Mills, on the north Devon coast, two large kiln structures survive. The eastern kiln bank, perched on the cliff edge, by a waterfall, dates from 1760 and had an inclined plane linking it with the hamlet above. This was its only access and it was one of the earliest cable-worked inclines or ramps in the south west. The gradient is steep: 1 in 1$\frac{1}{3}$.

At the foot of the ramp were two kilns. Limestone and culm were lowered down the plane and lime raised from the kilns by wheeled skips, hauled by a horse whim or capstan at the summit. Steps were set into the centre-line of the ramp to provide access for the limeburner.

Pack horses were employed to bring the limestone up to the top of the ramp from the beach. Here the stone was shipped from Caldy in small vessels and pitched overboard. When the tide ebbed, the limestone was collected. The whole process was rather labour intensive and Ernest Braund, who was born

in 1866, talking to Vernon Boyle in 1950, could not recall these kilns working in his time. So they had probably fallen out of use by 1870.

The inclined plane or ramp was extant in the 1960s. In the 1980s Torridge Council made the capstan platform at the head of the incline safe by employing specialist contractors to remove unstable strata. This involved the loss of the top section of the ramp.[6]

Chargot Wood, Langham Hill, Luxborough

SS 97463593 FOOT – SS 97733567 HEAD

At Chargot Wood on Langham Hill, near Gupworthy, prospecting for iron ores was undertaken in the 1830s. Work got underway in 1854 and from 1859 a narrow gauge incline facilitated the movement of ores from Bearland Wood Mine to a siding on the West Somerset Mineral Railway at Langham Hill. The length was 1,246 feet and the gradient 1 in 4. 12,000 tons of brown haematite were raised before closure. The incline was worked by one or more horse whims, possibly by a steam engine. Further developments here rendered the inclined plane redundant by 1867.[7]

Colton Pits, Nettlecombe

ST 050351 FOOT – ST 05203462 HEAD

At Colton Pits the Somerset Mineral Syndicate re-opened workings in 1907 and linked them to the West Somerset Mineral Railway by way of a 2-foot gauge tramway. From the West Colton Adit an 1,800-foot long inclined plane took the tramway 250 feet up to the high ground on Brendon Hill. It then ran 1$\frac{3}{4}$ miles to meet the mineral railway at the head of the Brendon inclined plane above Comberow. The Colton Pits plane was double track and worked by a stationary steam engine at its head. This was a two-cylinder steam winch with twin drums. In its brief period of operation the mine was

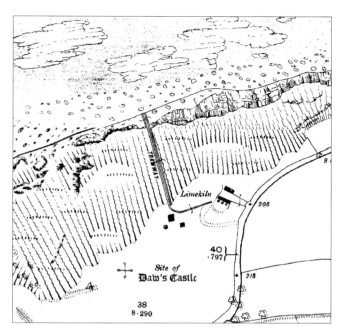

Brendon Hill Iron Mines. Twin-track narrow-gauge incline at Colton Pits, with the drum house above. *Somerset Industrial Archaeology Society*

Tramway from beach to limekilns at Daws Castle, Watchet, shown on the 1888 Ordnance Survey 1:2,500 map. *Old-Maps*

worked continuously with three eight-hour shifts. The ore here was not liked by the south Wales smelters; it tended to become hard cake in the Ebbw Vale furnaces. Closure came in 1910.[8]

Daws Castle Limekilns, Watchet
ST 06284331 HEAD, KILNS

A bank of limekilns was built on the cliffs to the west of the harbour in the mid nineteenth century, probably in the 1850s. The kilns belonged to the Wyndham estate and were in use in 1888. The limestone was collected from the shore reefs of lias and brought to the kilns by a narrow-gauge inclined tramway, which must have been powered; shown on the first edition 25-inch Ordnance Survey map. A survey by English Heritage indicates that one of three buildings at the top of the plane

may well have served as a winding house. Culm may also have been delivered to the kilns from vessels beached on the foreshore. The lower lias limestone here proved useful in the production of hydraulic cement. Limeburning was still undertaken, it seems, in 1929, although the tramway had been lifted and had been supplanted by road transport.[9]

Forestry plantation, Dulverton
SS 91402828 FOOT – SS 91452830 HEAD

A tramway is shown running up the steep-sided Barle valley to the north west of Dulverton town on a 25-inch Ordnance Survey map of 1904. It can only have been worked as an inclined plane, perhaps powered by a hand winch or possibly an oil engine. Much of the work may have been done by gravity.[10]

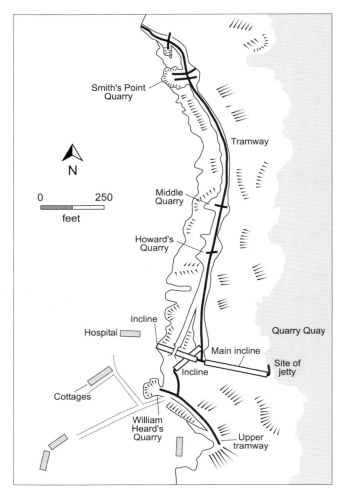

Lundy granite quarries and inclines. The main incline was probably constructed on trestle at its foot. Adapted from the 1886 Ordnance Survey map.

Lundy Island Granite Quarries
MAIN INCLINE: SS 13964505 FOOT – SS 13804507 HEAD

A short-lived venture was begun on Lundy Island in 1863. Five quarries were developed on the eastern side of the island, linked by a narrow-gauge tramway, using wooden rails. William Heard's quarry, above the southern end of the development, was linked via an upper platform to the main marshalling area 80 feet below by a self-acting inclined plane. This was crossed by a second incline running from a point by the hospital on the plateau to the marshalling area. It was a twin-track inclined plane with a gradient of 1 in 2.5. These two inclines may have been used in the preparation of the site and main incline. From the marshalling area a tramway ran northwards to connect with the other quarries. The main plane descended 260 feet at 1 in 1.5 to a jetty at Quarry Beach. It may well have been built on trestles at its foot: its formation disappears part way down the plane. By July 1865 three quarries were in operation and 90 tons of granite were being exported a week. The stone was shipped to Fremington Quay on the Taw estuary and, briefly, to Highbridge Quay. The operator, the Lundy Granite Co, was wound up in November 1868. The remoteness of the site made it economically unviable.

The quay and jetty at Quarry Beach have gone. Two circular revetments in granite at the head of the main incline, seen in 2008, are probably associated with the site of the winding drums.[11]

Lynton & Lynmouth Cliff Railway, Lynton and Lynmouth
SS721496 FOOT – SS 719496 HEAD

Most cliff railways are to be found on the coast. Almost the earliest was that linking Lynton and Lynmouth – the earliest was the Saltburn Cliff Lift, near Redcar. The Lynton funicular is unique in the south west: it works by water counterbalance. The project was funded by Sir George Newnes, publisher and politician, and was designed by George Croydon Marks in 1888.

The line rises 490 feet on a gradient of 1 in 1¾ and is 862 feet long; it was originally designed for passengers and freight. The twin-track, 3 foot 9 inch gauge, line opened in April 1890. The tracks are laid close together on the cliff and diverge at the halfway point to allow the two cars to pass one another.

The two cars each carry a 700 gallon water tank beneath the passenger deck. Water is piped from West Lyn at Lynbridge to a reservoir at Lynton. Here the car at the head of the incline has its tank filled. When the car reaches the foot of the incline, at Lynmouth, the water is partially discharged until the car is lighter than the one at Lynton, enabling that car, now also carrying water, to haul the ascending one up to Lynton. Newnes and Marks devised four braking systems; each car has two sets of brakes which are water operated.

The original scheme included a pier at Lynmouth to accommodate large paddle steamers, but this was never realised. The cliff railway is still in operation and Lynton is reached from Lynmouth in 1½ minutes.[12]

Lynton & Lynmouth Cliff Railway, one of the two cars at the head of the water counter-balance funicular, overlooking Lynmouth Bay.
Stephen Chatfield

Marsh Quarries, Marsh, Swimbridge
SS 61243012 QUARRY FLOOR – SS 61143018 HEAD

A now flooded limestone quarry was being worked in 1856 when a fatal accident occurred. A sixteen-year old youth named Kingdon, who was employed to tip wagons at the top of the incline, was crushed between a wagon and the 'pulley box'. The steam engine, which was used to work the incline, in taking up slack on the chain, over-wound the winding drum. The plane linked the quarry floor and the Marsh Lime Kilns via a tunnel. William Hartnoll was the owner at that time.[13]

A detail of the twin hydraulic braking systems installed on the Lynton & Lynmouth Cliff Railway cars. Two are friction brakes, steel blocks that press down on to the rail by hydraulic pistons. Water rather than oil is used. The others are hydraulic callipers; these clamp across the crown of the rails and were patented in 1888.

Newland Quarry, Exford
SS 82513851

Exmoor is virtually devoid of limestone, but an outcrop was found at Newland in Exford parish. This was worked as two deep quarries. A 25-foot diameter waterwheel, located underground, powered a cable drum at the head of the inclined plane in the larger eastern quarry. It also pumped water from the workings via a system of flat rods. The incline raised limestone 100 feet to five limekilns on the site. These provided the lime needed for the improvement of the poor Exmoor soils fostered by John and Frederick Knight. The eastern quarry was in operation in 1889 but the tramway had been lifted by 1903, although the 'Drum' or drumhouse was shown standing on the Ordnance Survey 1:2,500 map published that year. Quarries at Treborough were also worked for limestone and a cable-worked incline may also have existed there.[14]

North Light, Lundy. Supplies from the shore were raised by a cableway and then the single track incline seen here took them down to the lighthouse. *Michael Messenger*

North Light, Lundy
SS 131481

The lighthouse on Lundy island known as the North Light was built in 1897. Supplies were lowered down to the site by a single-track 2-foot gauge inclined plane which was worked by an electrically-powered winch. The line closed in 1980 when the lighthouse was automated.[15]

Nurcott Quarry, Luxborough
SS 96533888 WATERWHEEL; SS 96593884 LIMEKILN
SS 96523883 INCLINE

A limekiln serving Nurcott Quarry in Luxborough parish, in Somerset, was at work until 1932. Its plane was thought to be powered by a 15 foot by 3 foot overshot waterwheel.[16] The site has been remodelled, probably after 1902, making interpretation uncertain. An earlier incline shown on the 1888 map was worked, it appears, by a horse gin. Steel sleepers from the later plane indicate a gauge of 1 foot 8 inches. The waterwheel was removed for scrap in World War II.[17]

Oakhampton Quarry, Wiveliscombe
ST 085301

At Oakhampton the quarry was being worked for roofing slates by 1608. The incline was at surface and was worked from the early 1870s to about 1912, but not continuously: the quarry was disused in 1889 but at work in 1904. The plane was steam powered and narrow-gauge, at 2 foot. There was also an aerial ropeway, for which the base of the winding engine exists. The waste tips are now over-grown and the incline formation is lost in places.[18]

Rolle Canal – Ridd Incline, Monkleigh

SS 46302240

This was also known as the Torrington Canal. Denys Rolle wanted a canal to bring sea-sand inland to fertilise the poor acidic North Devon soils. Rolle died in 1797 before his ambition was realised and it was his son, Lord Rolle, who implemented the canal from Weare Giffard to Torrington with its single inclined plane. It was, like the Bude Canal, designed by James Green. Following the success of the canal at Bude, tub boats were again employed. Fully loaded, they weighed about six tons and the 220-foot long Ridd inclined plane lifted them 60 feet above the river Torridge. This was constructed as a twin-track incline and was powered by a 32 foot by 7 foot waterwheel at its summit. Tub boats ran up and down the incline on their own wheels. The plane was in operation from 1827 to 1870, when it disappeared under the formation of the railway from Torrington to Bideford. A full description of its operation is given by Barry Hughes:

Ridd Incline head. The waterwheel was in a pit below the canal, beneath the gantry. *North Devon Museum Trust*

'Only one loaded barge weighing a total of about six tons could be hauled up at a time, so the barge trains were moored up to the bank whilst the individual barges were worked over the incline. The horse was tethered so that the boy could help the boatman manoeuvre each boat under the endless chain where it dipped down into the canal. The incline keeper, operating the machinery at the top of the plane, would set the chain in motion when signalled. The boat was then pulled forward until one of the heavy links engaged in the metal-clad V-shaped notch set in the centre of the barge's bow. The chain now dragged the barge into alignment with the rails. As the barge moved forward, the boatman, riding on the cargo, had to insert the point of the plough-shaped hook, or 'dog', fastened to the stern of the boat by a chain bridle into a link of the moving chain. This dog held the boat on the endless chain as it was dragged at a steady walking pace out of the water and onto the 220-foot incline. The slow speed, about three miles per hour, allowed the boatman to jump off the moving boat and link up the next in line once the first one had cleared the top of the slope. The boatman would ride up the incline on the last boat, taking care to keep clear of the heavy dog when it was knocked from the chain by the overhead roller as the barge plunged over the upper sill into the water

of the upper pound. The boy, meanwhile, would ride the horse past another small riverside dock ..

From the dock the barge horse would .. emerge in a small hamlet .. In the days when the only large machines were wind or water mills, the working of the great wheel was quite a dramatic sight. The machinery, visible on the top of the incline, consisted of a massive oak framework which spanned the upper basin and its central island. This supported a horizontal wooden wheel 23 feet in diameter which drove the endless chain, together with its brake bands and guide pulleys and the levers which controlled it. The chain wheel revolved on a long vertical iron axle shaft which emerged from a hole in the central island. Hidden directly below the upper basin was a vast arched chamber which housed a water wheel 32 feet in diameter and 7 feet wide. This drove gearing in a side chamber and from this chamber the main vertical axle shaft emerged to drive the overhead chain wheel on the top of the incline.

Water to power the wheel was released from the canal through a sluice in the western side of the central island. The incline keeper controlling the machinery stood alongside the main shaft; he regulated the flow of water through the sluice with one lever, and used a much longer lever to operate the friction brake on the chain wheel. A cast iron bevelled cog mounted on the main drive axle also powered a smaller vertical chain wheel, which drove a lighter endless chain running along the western side of the central island. This was used for pulling boats heading down the incline up and over the curved sill which formed a dam at the end of the upper pound.

Nimble work was required of the boatman for this task of manoeuvring the boats onto the downward incline. He had to ensure that the main incline chain engaged in the bow notch to pull the boat onto the incline, and then he had to unhook the light side chain and hook the dog on the V-shaped stern bridle into the main chain. This provided a brake, preventing the boat from running away down the incline. A boatman on the Bude canal failed to do this in 1831 on the Hobbacott Down incline, and the boat ran away unchecked to crash intothe machinery and barges in the lower basin; luckily, no one was hurt.' [19]

Rolle Canal - a cutaway drawing of the Ridd incline head with its 32 foot by 7 foot waterwheel in a wheelpit beneath and between the two arms of the upper canal; its drive machinery to a 23-foot diameter horizontal wheel supported by a gantry above the incline allowing one boat to descend and a second to ascend. *Drawing by B. D. Hughes*

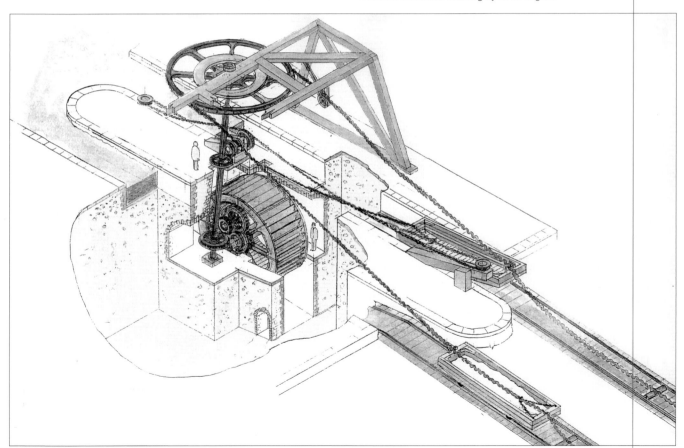

Rosemoor Limekilns, near Great Torrington
SS 498179

A bank of five limekilns was designed by James Green alongside the Rolle Canal, by New Town Mills, near Great Torrington. These were surveyed in 1968 and together with details in a photograph of circa 1870, indicate that they were served by an inclined plane or ramp, possibly worked by a horse gin. However there is some evidence to suggest that the incline was powered by the bucket-in-a-well system that James Green employed at Hobbacott Down, on the Bude Canal. The kiln bank was active in 1843-1875, but had been partly demolished by 1890.[20]

Venn Quarries, Landkey
SS587306

A. H. Slee, writing in 1938, described the quarry complex here: 'The most important lime-burning kilns in the Barnstaple area were at Venn in Landkey. Here two quarries were worked .. one now called Shebbear Pond, and the other ..Venn Pond. The kilns were on the left of Venn stream, and a viaduct ran from the quarry to the kilns. A water-wheel worked trolleys running to the kilns …Culm was used for burning, and this was imported from South Wales ….'

Locally mined culm from Tawstock and Chittlehampton was also used. The tramways linking the quarries and kilns were partly on inclined planes and the pits of the water-wheels which once used to power the plane from Shebbear Pond are still extant, as are an engine house and its chimney, used in later decades. As the quarries deepened, dewatering became an issue; originally two waterwheels by the Venn stream were installed for this purpose. The increasing cost of pumping the quarries and a decreasing demand for lime led to closure by the 1870s. By the 1890s the quarries were flooded. Today's Venn Quarry, to the south west, is on a much larger scale, run by Aggregate Industries plc, and some old workings have been lost under this new development.[21]

Venn Quarries, Landkey. Worked until the 1870s. Both main quarries were flooded by 1890 and Venn Quarry backfilled by 1970. From the Ordnance Survey 1:2,500 map of 1888. A nature trail now runs through the site. The present day Venn Quarry is to the south west, on the other side of Venn Bridge. *Old-Maps*

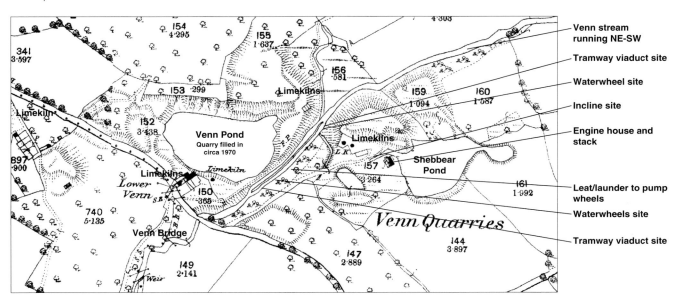

Dartmoor

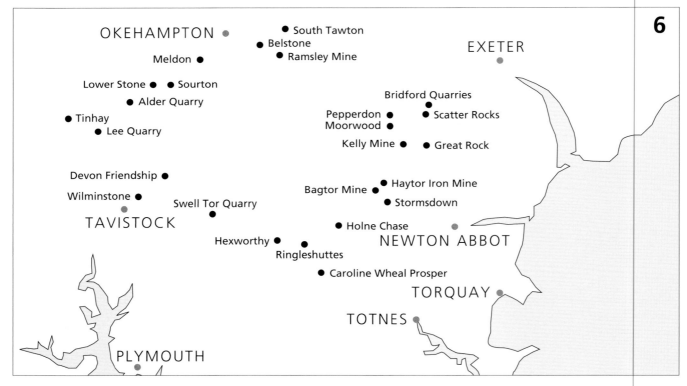

OKEHAMPTON ●
● South Tawton
● Belstone
● Ramsley Mine
EXETER ●

Meldon ●

Lower Stone ● ● Sourton
Bridford Quarries
● Alder Quarry
Pepperdon ● ● Scatter Rocks
● Tinhay
Moorwood ●
● Lee Quarry
Kelly Mine ● ● Great Rock

Devon Friendship ●
Bagtor Mine ● ● Haytor Iron Mine
Wilminstone ●
● Stormsdown
Swell Tor Quarry
TAVISTOCK ●
● Holne Chase
NEWTON ABBOT ●
Hexworthy ●
Ringleshuttes ●
● Caroline Wheal Prosper
TORQUAY ●
TOTNES ●
PLYMOUTH

6

Mines and quarries on Dartmoor once used inclined planes extensively. One or two, such as Caroline Wheal Prosper in Buckfastleigh parish, are in remote inaccessible valleys and most are on private land.

Kelly Mine, near Lustleigh, has a short narrow-gauge plane which can be seen when the site is open to the public.

Of the quarries, most are now flooded and the inclines either destroyed or no longer visible. Other inclined planes on Dartmoor await discovery.

This section also includes quarry sites to the north and west of Dartmoor, between Bridestowe and Lifton. For the south western edges of the moor see the section on South Devon and South-west Dartmoor.

Alder Quarry, near Lobhillcross, Thrushelton
SX 47558728 FOOT – SX 47638725 HEAD

A flooded limestone quarry lies by the old A30 turnpike road; it is now a nature reserve. In 1853 William Eastabrook obtained a 99-year lease on the site from John Morth Woollcombe of Ashbury. An inclined plane and tramway system were evident in 1884 but had mostly been lifted by 1905. The plane formation was still visible in the 1960s.[1]

Bagtor Mine, Ilsington
SX 764760 CROWNLEY PARKS, FOOT OF INCLINE
SX 762759 BAGTOR MINE

Dines, writing in 1956, recorded the workings here as little more than trials; a mere 15 tons of black tin were recovered in the period 1863-5. Hamilton Jenkin noted 25 tons of tin recovered. Longitudinal sections for the mine show three shafts. Two horse gins were used to raise ores and in 1863 a new 60-foot waterwheel was installed to pump the mine, via a long train of flat rods, and power the stamps. The sett was extensive, including workings near Hemsworthy Gate, Bagtor Mine to the south-east and Crownley Parks further east, also known as Mill Wood, where dressing floors were linked to the rest of the sett by a tramway 1¾ miles long. Approaching from the north, the tramway ran past Bagtor Cottages. It is now a footpath. To the east, on private land, a farm track diverges on the right, running steeply downhill. This was the formation of the inclined plane to the dressing floors, where a wheelpit exists. At the head of the plane the masonry platform for the incline's brake drum survives amongst the bracken. The plane was about 360 feet long. Closure came in 1866.[2]

Belstone Quarry, Belstone
SX 637943

This was a twentieth century excavation by the old trunk road from Whiddon Down to Okehampton, just north of Sticklepath County Primary School. It did not exist in 1905. A short incline from the quarry brought rock up to the plant by the main road, and at right angles to it, terminating just above it. A turntable, used to shift tubs to the plant, was extant in 1970, twenty years after the quarry had closed. It had served Devon County Council.[3]

Bridford Quarry, Bridford
SX 82878630 FOOT – SX 82788644 HEAD

Bridford Quarry, otherwise known as Paddy Dixon's, on the eastern flank of Dartmoor, was expanded before World War I. Around 1910 a narrow gauge tub line was built linking the three quarries in the complex with a crusher plant just beyond Stone Lane. The lower section of the route – perhaps 630 feet long – was on an inclined plane with a gradient of 1 in 4. From the crusher plant a standard gauge branch ran three-quarters of a mile to sidings by Christow station. The stone here was basalt; closure came circa 1932.[4]

Caroline Wheal Prosper, West Buckfastleigh
SX 69436559 AT SHAFT – SX 70116588 STAMPS

Caroline Wheal Prosper was a tin mine in a remote valley to the west of Buckfastleigh which was developed in 1854 and closed in 1859. It was not a success; despite being blessed with a 40 foot by 3 foot waterwheel and 24 head of stamps, only 10 hundredweight of tin was ever raised here. A tramway from the shaft on Lambs Down to the dressing floors by the Dean Burn was operated as an inclined plane. It was about 1,100 feet in length, with an average gradient of 1 in 2. The stone loading of the brake drum was still in-situ at the incline head in the early 1960s.[5]

Devon Friendship, Mary Tavy
SX 50787917 FOOT – SX 51187911 HEAD

In 1880 Wheal Friendship, at Mary Tavy, was renamed Devon Friendship and tin and arsenic ores were raised from Bennett's shaft. An inclined tramway was laid to dressing floors situated nearly half a mile north-north-west of Mary Tavy church. It only functioned for a few years and ceased

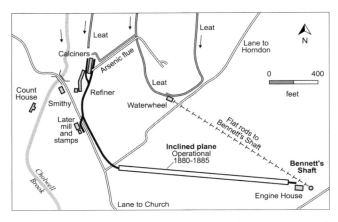

Devon Friendship, showing the inclined plane at surface, which operated from 1880-1885.

work in 1885. This was a gravity-operated incline and the rails were in place in 1932, as were the drum and brake gear at the head of the plane.[6]

Great Rock Mine, Hennock
SX 82808168 FOOT – SX82748157 HEAD

At least five twentieth-century iron mines on Dartmoor employed inclines. Great Rock Mine was worked from 1902 to 1969 and operated on six levels. Its micaceous haematite was used in the production of anti-corrosion paints: on structures such as Brunel's Royal Albert Bridge at Saltash. The ore was exported worldwide.

A 2-foot gauge single-track incline, about 300 feet long, was constructed in 1938. It took ores from No 4 Crosscut Level near the Beadon Brook to the mill, 100 feet or so higher up the valley. Motive power was a second-hand marine steam winch operating on compressed air. The operator, who also ran the mill, was alerted to wagons waiting to be hauled up the valley side by a piece of iron clanging against the roof of his shed, worked by a wire running up the hill from the incline foot. The winch, sited near the incline head, was unable to shut off suddenly, resulting in one or two incidents on the tramway. At other times the wire haulage rope frayed

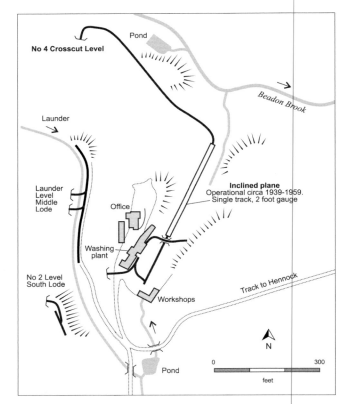

Great Rock Mine, Hennock, with the inclined plane linking No 4 Crosscut level in the valley with the mill, 100 feet or so higher up.

and broke. By 1960 mining had ceased on No 4 Crosscut level and the incline fell into disuse. It is now washed away in parts and overgrown.[7]

Haytor Iron Mine, Ilsington
SX 77387711 (MINE)

The mine, a little to the south of the Rock Inn, was originally opencast but accessed by an inclined shaft as early as 1827. Nearly a century later Haytor Iron Mines Ltd constructed an inclined plane 1,000 feet long from the adit level of their workings, a little to the east, to the Bovey Tracey road. This was in use from 1920 and in 1921 the mine's output was taken to Bovey Tracey railway station; the traction engine and trailer caused damage to the local roads.[8]

Hexworthy Mine, Dartmoor Forest
SX 65677086 HEAD

In the heart of the moor Hexworthy Mine was a combined working of the older Hensroost and Hooten Wheals mines, operated by John Taylor & Sons from 1889 until suspended in 1903. 136 tons of black tin were raised, worth £7,516. Further brief operations followed in 1905-1912 and 1915-1916. Ore was trammed out of an adit by Low's Shaft at Hooten Wheals; here trucks were connected one by one to a cable-worked single-track gravity incline. The ore-laden wagon hauled up and passed an empty truck at a half-way loop. The tramway ran roughly 1,700 feet to dressing floors at Dry Lake; trucks were manhandled over the last section. This route may have been abandoned in the 1905-1912 working.[9]

Holne Chase Mine, Holne
SX 715710 foot – SX 71837114 head

Holne Chase Mine was worked for tin in 1875-1878 but very little was recovered; it is on private land. A 1,400-foot incline forms part of a 3,165-foot-long tramway which linked the mine, 600 feet above sea level, with dressing floors by the Dart. It was single track, with a rise of 200 feet. The formation exists partly in shallow cutting, and is on embankment near the summit.[10]

Kelly Mine, Bovey Tracey
SX 795818

Kelly Mine worked micaceous haematite from 1879-1892 and 1900-1944. The surface features have survived here and are now cared for by the Kelly Mine Preservation Society. They include a short inclined plane which runs from the lower adit up to the ore washing area. The incline, which was in use in

Kelly Mine, in Bovey Tracey parish, near Lustleigh. The re-instated single-track incline. *KH, Mine-Explorer*

its original form up until 1944, was re-laid towards the end of the twentieth century by the society using 'modern' rails recovered from Morwellham Quay. The ore is wound uphill in small mine 'trams' using a very old winch powered by a water turbine or by a Blackstone oil engine. The rail gauge is 1 foot 6 inches.[11]

Lee Quarry, Marystow
SX 44058356

A limestone quarry with an extensive internal tramway system was in operation in 1884. An inclined plane, possibly double-track, ran roughly south-south-east from the quarry floor to a bank of limekilns at ground level. A second incline took waste to tips. A leat ran to the quarry, so that it is clear the workings benefitted from water power. Whether the incline was so powered is not known. The quarry was still at work, with the tramway in use, in 1906. By 1953 the quarry had become

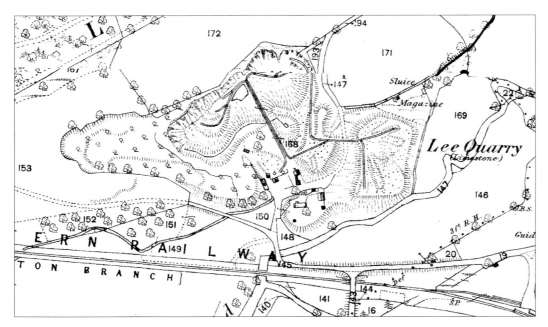

Lee Quarry, Marystow. A limestone quarry with an internal tramway system, seen on the 1:2,500 Ordnance Survey map of 1884. It was still at work in 1906. The inclined plane is thought to be the line running south-east in a straight line from the quarry floor. Note the leat coming in from top right and exiting the quarry towards the Launceston branch railway. It may have provided a power source for the workings, via a waterwheel or turbine.
Old-Maps

flooded and the kiln bank had gone. The site is close to the course of the GWR's Launceston branch, but there was no connection or interchange with the railway. It is now within a wood. A public footpath runs round the south-east perimeter.[12]

Lower Stone Quarry, Bridestowe
SX 50268903

Water power was necessary at the Lower Stone Quarry, Bridestowe, to haul wagons up from the workings. The site was for sale in 1839:

'.. To be Sold by Public Auction, for the remainder of a term of 38 years, from 1st day of January 1818, subject to the rent of £110 a year .. all that well-known Lime Quarry .. called LOWER STONE QUARRY .. situate in the parish of Bridestowe, now in the occupation of Mr George Robinson, the Proprietor. The right of working extends over a surface of upwards of 20 Acres. There are four kilns on the premises, with very extensive

Railways, Inclined Planes, and an Adit Level. There is one Water Engine of about 14 horse power, with all necessary machinery, in excellent condition for working the waggons up the inclined planes and pumping the water ..' [13]

In 1880 the quarry was offered for sale as part of the Millaton estate. Three tramway inclines took stone up from the the quarry floor in 1884.[14] The workings are now flooded.

Meldon Limekilns, Okehampton Hamlets
SX 56409218 FOOT – SX 56429225 HEAD

At Meldon, an inclined plane formed part of a narrow-gauge tramway system on the west bank of the West Okement, linking a large nineteenth-century limekiln with a now flooded limestone quarry. A second single-track inclined plane ran down from the railway to the valley floor, just east of Meldon Viaduct, and was apparently still in use in 1895. It can be seen on a Francis Frith photograph of the viaduct and limekiln, dated 1890. Both formations survive today.[15]

Moorwood, Moretonhampstead

SX 776837

At Moorwood, by the road from Bovey Tracey to Moretonhampstead and in the latter parish, deposits of micaceous haematite were found in 1931. The first ores were raised from this mine in the 1940s. Members of the now disbanded Exeter Industrial Archaeology Group recorded the remains of an inclined plane here worked by a hand winch in the 1970s. The plane was a short one, worked by gravity, from the mine's adit to the mill, on which a private house has since been built. Faint traces of the incline remain today.[16]

Pepperdon, Moretonhampstead

SX 778850

Pepperdon was another small micaeceous ore mine, to the north of Moorwood, on the valley side above Wray Barton, in Moretonhampstead parish: before 1885 the site was in Lustleigh. Surface works included a narrow-gauge inclined plane worked by a hand winch. Its rails and the winch were still in place in 1949.[17]

Ramsley Mine, South Tawton

SX 64969304 FOOT – SX65029305 HEAD

On the northern edge of Dartmoor, Ramsley Mine, in South Tawton parish, was worked for copper. It was at work from the 1850s until closure in 1909 and in 1885 was known as Emily Mine. A photograph taken in 1910 shows a twin-track inclined plane roughly in line with a large waterwheel near its foot. The plane was almost certainly self-acting; the waterwheel was used to crush ores brought down the incline.[18]

Ringleshuttes Mine, Holne Moor, Holne

SX 67566987 – SX 67797023

Some tin was raised from this opencast working in 1854-55, also known as Holne Moor Mine. A 1,300-foot long inclined

Ramsley Copper Mine, South Tawton, early in the twentieth century. An inclined plane can be seen running down towards the road at the foot of the spoil heaps, by the old building with the large waterwheel. *The Dartmoor Archive/South Tawton and District Local History Group.*

tramway ran from the engine shaft towards the dressing floors, terminating 390 feet short of them, and the formation is still extant.[19]

Scatter Rocks, Bridford

SX 82288563 HEAD – SX 82638598 FOOT

At Scatter Rocks a 2-foot gauge tub line ran from the Summit Quarry to a crusher plant at Lower Quarry; it was largely on a double-track inclined plane, about 1,540 feet long, probably self-acting. The quarry was worked by Scatter Rocks Macadams Ltd, Bridford until taken over by Roads Reconstruction (1934) Ltd. An aerial ropeway linked the crusher and Lower Quarry with Christow Station on the GWR branch from Heathfield to Exeter. Closure came after World War II: the plant was dismantled in 1953.[20]

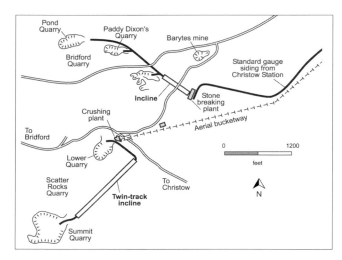

Bridford and Scatter Rocks Quarries and their connections to Christow Station on the GWR's Teign Valley branch line. Two inclined planes are shown.

Sourton Quarry, Bridestowe

SX 524895

Jack Palmer was the owner of this site in 1838 when he planned the quarry's development and made provision for a bank of four large limekilns, iron rails and stabling for pack animals. Three massive kilns were actually built. A waterwheel and a steep inclined plane were at work in 1865-1872, to bring limestone up to limekilns and tips at ground level. The quarry was occupied by Messrs Rowes and Crocker when auctioned as part of the Millaton estate in 1880; together with the kilns and spoil heaps it then covered 22 acres. The site is now a flooded pit.[21]

South Tawton Quarry, South Tawton

SX 65659507 CENTRE OF PLANE

A major limestone quarry. Twenty-five quarrymen were employed in 1841; this figure had dropped to six or so by 1881: J. D. Palmer leased the site from at least January 1870 through to December 1883. Narrow gauge railways were employed to haul the stone from the workings and the system included an inclined plane.[22]

Stormsdown, Ilsington

SX 772736 FOOT – SX 768729 HEAD

Stormsdown was a twentieth-century mining venture in Ilsington parish. The main shaft was sunk from a site 600 feet above sea level, not far from Owlacombe Cross and from 1906 to 1912 some tin and arsenic were mined here. A tramway ran down to Owlacombe Bridge, 180 feet below, and incorporated an inclined plane, probably 2-foot gauge, gravity-operated, single-track, with a passing loop.[23]

'When the mine went into production circa 1907 it was – for its time – extremely well-equipped. The mill .. was placed approximately one third of a mile from the shaft ... the ore was loaded underground into large side-tipping trams .. The trams were hoisted in the cage to the shaft-head and then lowered down the hillside via the incline plane to the rear of the mill where the ore would have been side-tipped over a grizzley placed above the main ore-bin.' A jaw-crusher by the foot of the grizzley dealt with oversize material. *'There was, therefore, no double-handling of the ore after it was loaded into a tram from the ore-pass beneath a working stope until it was in the ore-bin behind the stamps .. The mine – almost entirely*

South Tawton Quarry, by the head of an incline, foreground. A narrow gauge track can be seen beyond it, lower right. *Dartmoor Archive/South Tawton Local History Group*

electrically powered – was worked 24 hours a day and .. was extensively flood-lit.'

Communication between shaft and mill was probably effected by a bell system, known as a 'knocker line'. The inclined plane was 1,800 feet long and was still recognisable under gorse in 1949.[24]

Swell Tor Quarries, Walkhampton
SX 56217295 FOOT – SX 56207319 HEAD

At Swell Tor, on Dartmoor, an inclined plane serving the quarries there was visited by the Reverend Bray of Tavistock in 1831:

'an inclined plane of great breadth on which massy chains running upon rollers, and extending to a considerable distance up to the tor .. it was connected with two immense cranes, by which the workmen were then employed in poising and depositing on their unwieldy carriages the blocks of granite taken from what might be called a regular quarry.'

The product was used for the construction of Plymouth breakwater and naval docks at Devonport and Portsmouth. When the Princetown branch line replaced the Plymouth and Dartmoor tramway this twin-track self-acting plane was redundant: new sidings were laid into the quarry.[25]

Tinhay Quarry, Lifton
SX 395851 HEAD – SX 395852 FOOT

Tinhay Quarry developed on either side of the main road through the village. The two halves of the limestone quarry were linked by a tramway which ran on incline, crossing the road and the GWR's Launceston branch line. Functioning in 1888, the workings were disused by 1907. The 90-foot deep quarry to the north is now a fishing lake belonging to the Arundel Arms, Lifton. To the south of the road and course of the railway was the waste tipping area; this is now overgrown. A further incline site existed at nearby Lifton Quarry, SX 375845. This is now water-filled.[26]

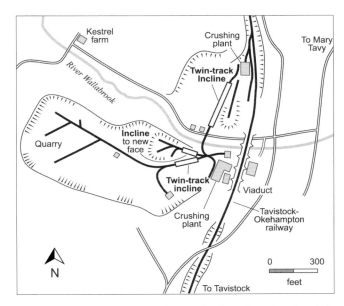

Wilminstone Quarry, near Tavistock. Site plan from circa 1951, by which time the site had three inclined planes. The quarry adjoined the railway from Okehampton to Tavistock.

Wilminstone Quarry, Tavistock
SX 490755 – INCLINE TO RAILWAY
SX 490754 – INCLINE ON WEST SIDE OF VALLEY

An elvan quarry was developed alongside the London & South Western Railway's line from Exeter to Plymouth at Wilminstone. A quarry, begun in 1890, was taken over by Devon County Council for roadstone in 1920. In 1922 a 2-foot gauge tramway was laid in to link the quarry in the valley with a crusher plant built by the side of the main line railway. A twin-track 1,450-foot long inclined plane brought stone up from the quarry to the crusher. A second double-track incline was constructed from the west side of the valley to the main quarry. The complex used to supply 1,200 tons of roadstone a week but is now closed and the quarry a flooded pit. The track was lifted in 1952.[27] In 2008 there were plans by West Devon Council to raise the quarry floor and turn the site into a boating lake.

South Devon and South-west Dartmoor

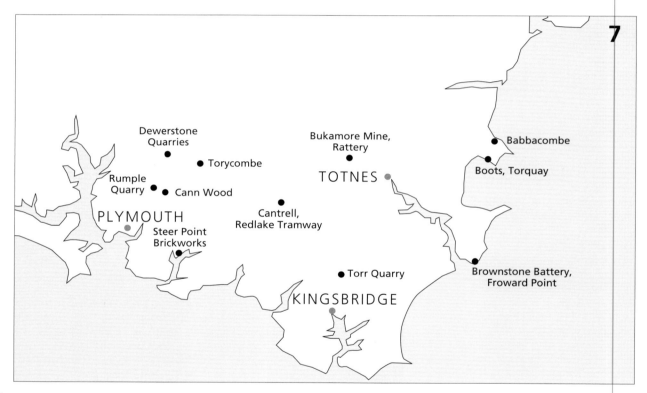

This section is largely devoted to sites in the local government districts of Torbay and the South Hams.

A good mix of sites can be found here: a cliff railway at Torquay, a military plane at Kingswear and a mine at Rattery. China clay works and their associated infrastructure include the remains of a long incline plane at Cann Wood.

Quarries feature at Torr in Woodleigh parish and in the Plym valley. At Rumple a 50 foot by 6 foot waterwheel worked a short plane from the quarry for a year before being abandoned in favour of steam power. Its impressive wheelpit overlooks the river Plym, by a public footpath.

At Steer Point, Brixton, an inclined plane once served a brickworks by the Yealm estuary and at Torquay one serves Boots the Chemist.

Babbacombe Cliff Lift, St Marychurch, Torbay
SX 92616577 FOOT – SX 92406574 HEAD

Sir George Newnes, the promoter of the cliff railways at Lynton, Bridgnorth and Clifton, first proposed a plane to Oddicombe beach, Torquay, in 1890. His concept initially met with fierce opposition but the line was eventually constructed between 1924-1926. It is twin track, 5 foot 8 inch gauge, 720 feet long with a rise of 256 feet, and an average gradient of 1 in 2.83, and powered by a electric motor. The consulting engineer was George Croydon Marks and the contractor the Waygood Otis Company.

Refurbished in 1951 and again in 2005, the inclined plane is now operated by Babbacombe Cliff Railway Community Interest Company for Torbay Council. It is usually open from Easter to the end of September.[1]

Boots, Torquay
SX 918636

A little-known incline is in Torquay. This single-track electrically-operated narrow-gauge tramway is purely for freight, and links Boots the Chemist, Strand, with The Terrace, Torquay.[2]

Brownstone Battery, Froward Point, Kingswear
SX 902496

The Royal Engineers were active at Froward Point in World War II. Gun emplacements were constructed here to defend the entrance to Dartmouth harbour. A 2-foot gauge tramway incline linked the battery with ammunition bunkers higher up the cliff. Rails on the twin-track winch-hauled incline were still in place in 2011.[3]

Babbacombe Cliff Lift to Oddicombe Beach, Torquay. *Sarah Charlesworth, under a Creative Commons Licence*

Brownstone Battery, Kingswear. Inclined plane to ammunition bunkers at Froward Point. *Dave Bellamy*

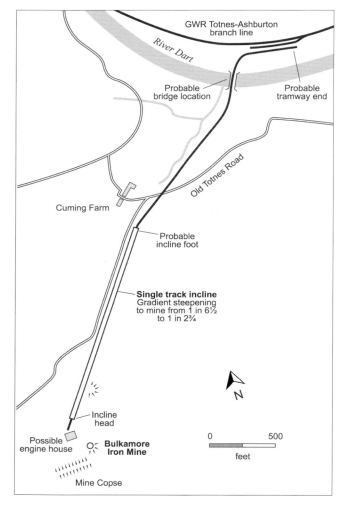

Bulkamore Mine, Rattery. The inclined plane formed the southern section of the tramway.

Bulkamore Mine, Rattery

SX 75136347 FOOT, ESTIMATED – SX 74906306 HEAD

Bulkamore Mine was remarkably short lived: it functioned from 1874-1875, high on a hillside. Its inclined plane, taking iron ores down to the Dart valley, was probably 1,200 feet long, possibly 1,550 feet, and was single track. The tramway was possibly 3-foot gauge, descending at 1 in 2¾ from the mine towards Cuming Farm where the gradient eased to 1 in 6½: its route is shown as 'disused' on the first edition 6" Ordnance Survey map of the area published in the 1880s. After running through a cutting the line crossed the Old Totnes Road and the ore trucks may then have descended purely by gravity to sidings by the Totnes-Ashburton branch in the Dart valley, then operated by the South Devon Railway. 4,000 tons of brown haematite were raised before closure.[4]

Dewerstone Quarries, Meavy

SX 53606405 FOOT – SX53706425 HEAD

Near the confluence of the Plym and Meavy a tramway was constructed to serve granite quarries close to the Dewerstone rocks. A 1,120 foot long inclined plane connects the upper and lower levels of this system and parts of its drum house and many stone sleeper blocks remain. The incline was active from 1858 and was standard gauge.[5] It is walkable today.

Dewerstone Quarries, Plym Valley. The formation of the inclined plane remains, with stone sleeper blocks in place.

Lee Moor Tramway
Cann Wood Incline, Sparkwell
SX 530590 FOOT – SX 538594 HEAD

Torycombe Incline, Sparkwell
SX 56506112 FOOT – SX 56936155 HEAD

In 1854 the Lee Moor Tramway was constructed to link china clay works at Wotter and Cholwichtown with quays at Plymouth. It included two self-acting inclines, both of which were reconstructed in 1858 following accidents. The Cann

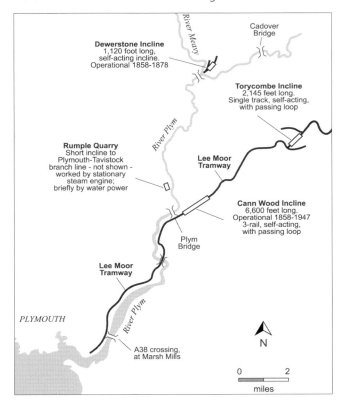

A diagram showing the location of four inclined planes in the Plym and Meavy valleys. There were two significant planes on the Lee Moor Tramway and others at Rumple Quarry and at the Dewerstone quarries. Standard-gauge railways and roads in the district have been omitted for clarity.

Wood incline, the lower of the two, was 6,600 feet long - 1¼ miles at 1 in 11. At Torycombe the plane was 2,145 feet long, with a gradient of 1 in 7. Both planes were single-track with a passing loop; but the upper section of the Cann Wood incline was configured as 3-line with a centre common rail. Below the loop at Torycombe track was interlaced for a section; this layout was used again at Cann Wood, where the incline crossed a road on a viaduct with restricted width, near its foot. At the head of the inclines, at the drum houses, the line reverted to twin-track formation. Track was laid out to the 4 foot 6 inch Dartmoor gauge, as the route was a branch of the earlier Plymouth and Dartmoor railway, built in 1823. Because of the length of the inclines wire ropes were used to haul and lower wagons.

At Cann Wood, five loaded trucks would pull up two loaded and three empty wagons. Speed of descent was controlled by a brakewheel at the drumhouse. Water tank wagons were used on the Torycombe incline to haul up loaded trucks. Traffic here was controlled by a system of bell signals between the brakesman at the head and the banksman at the foot of the plane. The line had closed by 1940.[6]

The drums at the head of the Cann Wood incline appear to remain underneath the embankment at the head of the plane. The course of the railway at its summit is accessible.

Lee Moor Tramway, Cann Wood Incline. Twin tracks leading to interlaced track on the viaduct beyond. Seen in 1923.
F. H. C. Casbourn/The Stephenson Locomotive Society

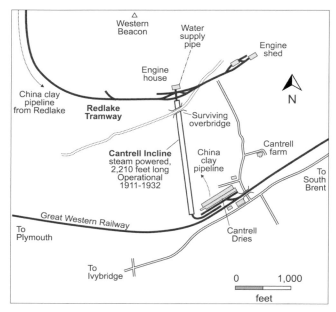

Redlake Tramway. The incline at Cantrell, near Ivybridge. The Redlake Tramway runs in from the north; the incline descends southwards to dries at Cantrell by the main line between Ivybridge and South Brent.

Redlake Tramway, Ugborough

SX 658566 FOOT – SX656571 HEAD

A twentieth-century enterprise on Dartmoor involved the construction of the 3-foot gauge Redlake Tramway which connected china clay pits at Redlake, remote in the heart of Dartmoor and 1,475 feet above sea level, with dries at Cantrell, with a siding alongside the Great Western Railway's main line near Ivybridge. The narrow-gauge railway was seven miles long and at its southern end descended 310 feet over a 2,210-foot long cable-worked incline, which appears to have been single track. China clay was piped to the dries; the railway was used to transport men and materials. An engine house at the head of the incline contained a 4-foot 6-inch diameter winding drum and a 12 horse-power steam engine, its water piped from the Lud Brook.

At the pit a second double-track incline took waste to a sky tip. Here the engine house was at the foot of the incline and contained a 14 horse-power double-cylinder Davey Paxman steam engine. Two 1,500 foot long cables coiled onto 4-foot diameter friction winding drums. This incline was worked using bell codes. A pit man rang his buddy at the summit: a single bell indicated stop truck; two - go slow and three: go. The railway and works operated from September 1911 to 1932.[7]

The top of the incline at Cantrell is still visible, where a bridge crosses it, and is accessible from a lane off the Ivybridge-South Brent road. The sky tip and flooded pit at Redlake are seven miles away. These are reached by foot or mountain bike along the railway formation.

Redlake Tramway. Top of the incline at Cantrell, now overgrown. *G Boddy/Dartmoor Archive*

Rumple Quarry, Plym valley

SX 52385968 WHEELPIT
SX 52285962 FOOT – SX 52265970 HEAD

Rumple quarry, near Plym Bridge, started life in the late eighteenth century. From about 1830 its slate was taken steeply uphill by horse and cart to the Plymouth and Dartmoor Railway and thence to quays at Plymouth. In 1864 The Plym River Slab and Slate Company acquired the lease together with the larger Cann Quarry across the valley. A short inclined plane was constructed to take the slate up to the Plymouth-Tavistock branch railway; it was powered by a steam engine. In an attempt to reduce running costs a 50-foot by 6-foot waterwheel was substituted. It was installed in a pit below the quarry and powered the plane by means of flat rods. The waterwheel, despite its size, was not a success and the steam engine was brought back into use in 1865. The company went into liquidation in 1866. The site is now within the National Trust's Plym Bridge Woods estate. The engine house survives as a ruined shell at the head of the incline.[8]

Rumple Quarry, Plym valley. Wheelpit for 50-foot by 6-foot breastshot waterwheel to work the inclined plane from the quarry.

Steer Point Brickworks, Brixton

SX 545502 FOOT – SX 546503 HEAD

Late in the nineteenth century high quality clay deposits were found at Steer Point, by the Yealm estuary in Brixton parish. These were developed by the South Hams Brickworks, with the quarry linked to the works by a twin-track 1 foot 6 inch gauge cable-worked tramway incline, which was in tunnel at the end nearest the quarry. A second tramway led from the brickworks to a quay on the estuary; here bricks were shipped and coal for the kilns imported. In 1900 this operation had been largely superseded by a siding laid in from the Great Western's Yealmpton branch, which remained open for freight until 1960.

By 1930 the concern was managed by Western Counties Brick Company and the incline from the quarry remained in use until 1953. The entire site was mothballed in 2008.[9]

Torr Quarry, Woodleigh

SX 744483 FOOT – SX 746481 HEAD

Ordnance Survey maps published in 1955 and 1969 show a 750-foot long tramway incline linking the quarry to what appears to be a workshop area. The tramway runs straight, in a south-easterly direction from the quarry floor.[10]

The Lower Tamar Valley
and South-east Cornwall

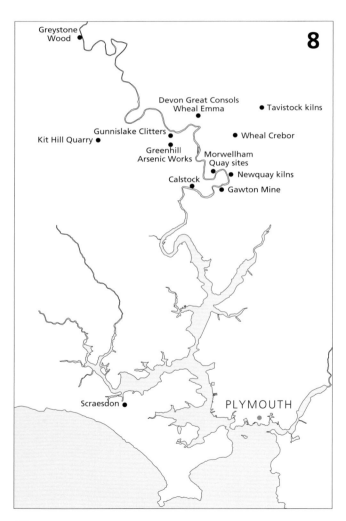

Greystone Wood ●

8

Devon Great Consols
Wheal Emma ●

● Tavistock kilns

Gunnislake Clitters ●
Kit Hill Quarry ●

Greenhill
Arsenic Works ●

● Wheal Crebor

Morwellham
Quay sites

Calstock ●

● Newquay kilns

● Gawton Mine

Scraesdon ●

PLYMOUTH

The remains of a once intensively worked industrial landscape can be found on the banks of the Tamar near Calstock and Gunnislake. Inclined planes were operated extensively here. John Taylor was responsible for the earliest – the plane linking the Tavistock Canal with Morwellham Quay. Copper ores from mines around Tavistock and Mary Tavy were shipped out to smelters at Swansea via the canal, its plane and the Tamar. Coal and iron ore were brought in by the same route. Tavistock iron foundries exported their steam engines to be used on more distant mines by this route. Morwellham Quay, its water-powered plane and canal to Tavistock provided the impetus for other enterprises. Planes came to link mines, quarries and limekilns – including the notably successful Devon Great Consols – with the river and its quays.

This section also includes the late Victorian incline running up to Scraesdon Fort on the military railway from Wacker Quay, on the Lynher estuary, to Tregantle.

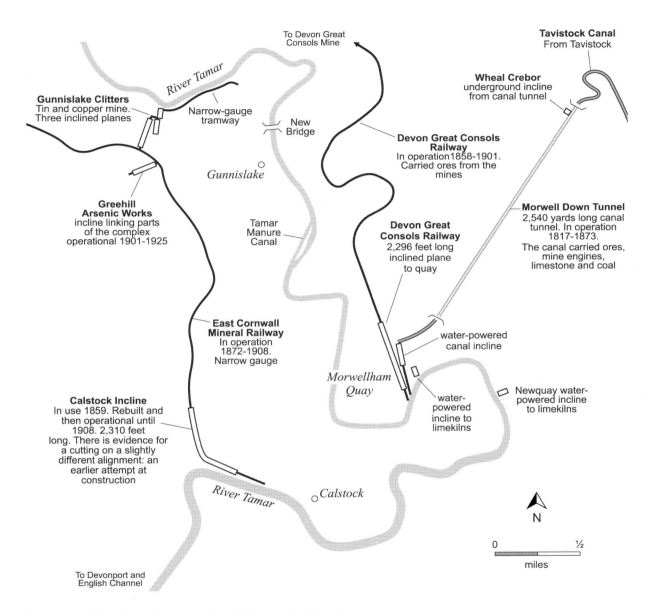

Tavistock Canal
From Tavistock

Wheal Crebor
underground incline
from canal tunnel

River Tamar

Gunnislake Clitters
Tin and copper mine.
Three inclined planes

Narrow-gauge
tramway

New
Bridge

Gunnislake

**Devon Great Consols
Railway**
In operation 1858-1901.
Carried ores from the
mines

To Devon Great
Consols Mine

**Greehill
Arsenic Works**
incline linking parts
of the complex
operational 1901-1925

Tamar
Manure
Canal

**Devon Great
Consols Railway**
2,296 feet long
inclined plane
to quay

Morwell Down Tunnel
2,540 yards long canal
tunnel. In operation
1817-1873.
The canal carried ores,
mine engines,
limestone and coal

**East Cornwall
Mineral Railway**
In operation
1872-1908.
Narrow gauge

water-powered
canal incline

*Morwellham
Quay*

Calstock Incline
In use 1859. Rebuilt and
then operational until
1908. 2,310 feet
long. There is evidence for
a cutting on a slightly
different alignment: an
earlier attempt at
construction

water-
powered
incline to
limekilns

Newquay water-
powered incline
to limekilns

River Tamar

Calstock

N

0   ½
miles

To Devonport and
English Channel

Inclined planes at Morwellham, Calstock and Gunnislake in the Tamar valley

Calstock Incline, East Cornwall Mineral Railway

Calstock Incline and the
East Cornwall Mineral Railway, Calstock

SX 42856887 FOOT – SX 426695 HEAD

Calstock Incline was financed by the Tamar Coal, Manure & General Mercantile Co. and opened in 1859. It was fully operational in 1860. Supplies to mines on the higher ground were hauled up from quays on the navigable river Tamar. The incline was single track at the foot, with a passing loop and a common three-rail section above it. It was 2,310 feet long with a gradient of 1 in 6. It was self-acting although a semi-portable stationary steam engine assisted the haulage of wagons 350 feet up from the quays, each with a load of 3 tons, usually two at time. The halfway loop was manned by a signal boy who was required to:

'…pay particular attention to the wire rope, pulleys, rollers, points, etc., and waggons passing up or down and, should anything go wrong, he must immediately signify the same by putting his Semaphore Signal at danger and by raising and violently waving his Red flag to the Signalman at the top of the incline, who in his turn, will, in the same manner as last described, signal to the engineman to stop hauling. Should these signals by any means be unobserved attention will be attracted by shouting or any other available method…'

Work over the plane ceased in fog or snow, nor was it worked at night. Eventually the plane formed the eastern end of the 7½ mile long, 3 foot 6 inch gauge, East Cornwall Mineral Railway, opened in 1872 to Kelly Bray near Callington.[1]

Calstock incline closed in 1908 after the London & South Western Railway had taken over the mineral railway, rebuilt it to standard gauge and re-routed part of it, taking the line over the Tamar on Calstock viaduct. A wagon lift by the side of the viaduct replaced the incline, but the new line to Bere Alston and Devonport effectively sidelined the river traffic.

East Cornwall Mineral Railway quays with, to the left, limekiln and Calstock incline, its foot on trestle. There is evidence for an earlier formation to the south west: a blind cutting exists above the Danescombe Hotel on private land, at ST 42690 68928. At its foot the ground level has been raised onto a walled embankment. The reason for its abandonment is not known. *Private collection, from an old postcard*

Devon Great Consols, Gulworthy

There were at least three inclined planes associated with this very successful copper mine in the nineteenth century. Two more were brought into use during a re-working for arsenic in the 1920s. One of these linked Wheal Fanny with Wheal Anna Maria (SX 426732) and was short-lived; disused by 1925.[2]

WHEAL EMMA: SX 43707357 FOOT – SX 439737 HEAD
WHEAL EMMA – NEW SHAFT: SX 43707345 FOOT – SX 438735 HEAD
WHEAL JOSIAH: SX 42777359 FOOT – SX 43157362 HEAD

Wheal Emma had a twin-track, standard gauge incline, which connected with the main mine railway via a siding, and this was both steam-powered and self-acting. It was probably in use from 1858 to 1903. The formation is well preserved.
A short single-track incline on an embanked trackbed, just to the south, was operational in 1884. It junctioned with the foot of the Wheal Emma branch of the mine railway and terminated by the New Shaft. Full wagons were probably gravity worked down the incline, with a now vanished drum house at its head. Empties were hauled up by the nearby whim engine.[3]

By 1850 Wheal Josiah had a self-acting, twin-track incline to take copper ore down to dressing floors at Anna Maria. It replaced transport by horse and cart and was 1,200 feet in length.[4]

Wheal Emma and its inclined plane to the Devon Great Consols Railway. *Private collection*

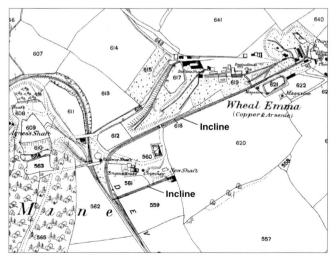

Devon Great Consols. Inclines at Wheal Emma. From the Ordnance Survey 1:2,500 map of 1884. *Old-Maps*

The present-day remains of the incline to New Shaft, Wheal Emma: a raised single-track formation under trees. *Rick Stewart*

Morwellham Quay, on the banks of the river Tamar. Photographed from the Cornish bank in circa 1868. The port is a hive of activity, with piles of copper ore waiting to be shipped to smelters at Swansea. Above the group of semi-detached cottages can be seen the line of the Devon Great Consols Railway Incline descending to the quay. It is in tunnel at the foot, before running out onto trestles above the quays. Immediately to the right of this incline can be seen the formation of the incline that linked the terminus of the Tavistock Canal (qv) with the quay.

Devon Great Consols Railway, incline to Morwellham Quay, Gulworthy

SX 4453 6957 FOOT – SX 4428 7035 HEAD

In 1858 the four-and-a-half-mile-long Devon Great Consols railway opened, linking this major copper mine to Morwellham Quay on the river Tamar. It was standard gauge. Above Morwellham a single-track incline with a passing loop dropped 2,296 feet – a little under half a mile, at 1 in 3 – from the down to a new quay, running through a short tunnel at its foot. It was worked by a 22-inch stationary steam engine – built at the mine foundry – at the head of the plane. This required water which was supplied by a 25-foot diameter waterwheel pumping in lifts from the Tavistock Canal. The two-ton five-hundredweight ore wagons carried a three-and-a-half-ton load and in ideal circumstances the incline was self-acting: two descending wagons would bring up two empties. But coal and timber were brought up the incline for use at Devon Great Consols, Bedford United and other mines. The steam engine was on hand to assist, and was connected to a huge drum which wound the 4-inch thick wire rope used for haulage. The incline was out of use by 1901.[5] Part of the formation is accessible: but the head of the plane is on private land.

Gawton Mine, Gulworthy

SX 452687

Arsenic was mined at Gawton, where copper ores had previously been won. The workings were reconfigured in 1894-6 and included an inclined tramway. But following completion, the market for arsenic collapsed and it is possible that the tramway was never used. The operator, Devon Gawton Co, closed the mine in 1902 and the company was liquidated in 1903.[6]

Greenhill Arsenic Works, Gunnislake, Calstock
SX 42207179 FOOT – SX 42017172 HEAD

The East Cornwall Mineral Railway opened in 1872 and this works was probably constructed within the next two years. It was a major concern, straddling the Gunnislake-Chilsworthy road and the railway, to which it was linked by sidings. The site spread over several acres on a hill slope – in addition to arsenic processing, there was a tin smelting plant and a brickworks – and the upper and lower halves were linked by a cable-worked inclined plane. Closure came in 1925. Ruined buildings were still extant in 1999.[7]

Greystone Wood Manganese Mine, Lezant
SX 362794 SHAFTS

At Greystone Wood, on the banks of the Tamar in Lezant parish, a sett was let in 1840 and again in 1885 to search for manganese, tin and other minerals. Greystone Wood Manganese Syndicate Ltd, of Liverpool was authorised by the local farmer to lay a tramway from the mine in 1907. This line incorporated an inclined plane. The incline winding drum and rusting cables were still in situ in 1970.[8]

Gunnislake Clitters Mine, Calstock
WESTERN TRAMWAY: SX 42067193 HEAD – SX 42177225 FOOT
EASTERN TRAMWAY: SX 42227208 HEAD – SX 42267235 FOOT

Gunnislake Clitters was a tin and copper mine situated on a steep north-facing slope above the river Tamar. First worked in the 1820s, the mine was fully active from 1858, raising 33,310 tons of copper ore by 1904.
By 1900 it was re-processing waste dumps. Work ceased then, but the during World War I the mill was used to process wolfram brought by aerial ropeway from workings on Kit Hill and Hingston Down.
This phase saw the introduction of inclined plane tramways. These were constructed to the 3 foot 6 inch gauge. The western incline was double track and linked the mill with the East Cornwall Mineral Railway above it. Shallow cuttings and stone-faced embankments were necessary to create the formation. It was about 2,000 feet long with a rise of 350 feet and worked by a stationary steam engine. It crossed two lanes on bridges; the upper buttress on the top road may have supported the winding drums. Coal and ore were sent down the incline to the processing plant, possibly by gravity, and processed ore hauled up.
The eastern incline was single track, and ran down from adit level to the mill. A lower section, not quite aligned, with a drum house at its head, linked the mill with the tramway to Hawkmoor on the bank of the Tamar. This was also powered by a stationary steam engine.[9] The inclined tramways are clearly shown on the 1:2,500 Ordnance Survey map of 1908. The works closed in 1918. The western tramway is hidden under vegetation, whereas the eastern tramway is largely clear of it, but within a now wooded hillside.

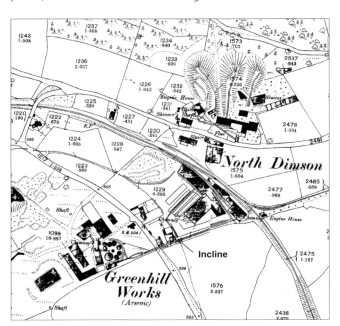

Greenhill Works and its inclined plane crossing the Gunnislake-Chilsworthy road, with the East Cornwall Mineral Railway at the incline foot. From the Ordnance Survey 1:2,500 of 1883-1901. *Old-Maps*

Gunnislake Clitters processing mill early in the twentieth century – about 1903. Looking south. Inclined tramways are visible to the left of the mill building: these are the eastern inclined planes. A third inclined plane linked the mill with the East Cornwall Mineral Railway, running uphill. It was extant in 1908. *Royal Institution of Cornwall*

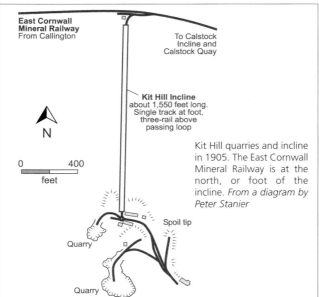

East Cornwall Mineral Railway
From Callington

To Calstock Incline and Calstock Quay

Kit Hill Incline
about 1,550 feet long. Single track at foot, three-rail above passing loop

N

0   400
feet

Kit Hill quarries and incline in 1905. The East Cornwall Mineral Railway is at the north, or foot of the incline. *From a diagram by Peter Stanier*

Spoil tip

Quarry

Quarry

Kit Hill Quarry, Stoke Climsland
SX 37407228 FOOT – SX 37487178 HEAD

The Kit Hill inclined plane was constructed to link granite quarries on Kit Hill with the 3 foot 6 inch gauge East Cornwall Mineral Railway, which opened in 1872. This plane was self-acting, about 1,600 feet long with its gradient 1 in 8 at the foot, 1 in 5 at its head. Rock was lowered 300 feet from the quarries at the top of the hill to the railway at Downgate sidings. Kit Hill granite was used in six London bridges – London, Chelsea, Putney, Lambeth, Blackfriars, Waterloo, and at Devonport, Millwall Docks and the Bishop Rock Lighthouse in the Scilly Isles. This was all shipped out via the incline and quays at Calstock. Closure came in 1955; track having been converted to standard gauge in the late 1930s. It was single track at the foot and three-rail above the passing loop: the central section of the plane was on embankment.[10] The incline is walkable; there is a car park at its foot. Quarries at the summit now form part of the Kit Hill Country Park.

Kit Hill inclined plane today.

Morwellham hydro-electric power station, Gulworthy
SX 44746982 FOOT – SX 44746992 HEAD

In 1934 a temporary single-track narrow gauge incline was used during the construction of the pipeline serving the power station, linking it with the Tavistock Canal above. The station still supplies electricity to the National Grid today.

Morwellham Quay Limekilns, Gulworthy
SX 44666976

In 2005 excavations at Limekiln Quay, Morwellham, on the banks of the Tamar, revealed the remains of two wooden turntables and plate rails, together with the foundations of an incline ramp, which have been dated to 1816-1817. The bank of limekilns at Morwellham Quay, which they served, remain today.

Limekilns vary in size from small 5-tonners to 20-ton pots. Those at Morwellham and Newquay, a little downstream, are large and by incorporating an inclined plane to take culm and limestone to the charging bank at the top of the kilns, some of the limeburner's heavy work was mechanised: the inclined planes were water-powered. At Morwellham the waterwheel was 30 foot by 2 foot 6 inches; the rail gauge was 4 foot 3 inches or 4 foot 3½ inches. Gill and Company ran this kiln bank until 1869. The water-powered ramp enabled these kilns to be worked continuously; coal shutes were let into the sides of the pots until a rebuilding circa 1850. Between 1873 and 1885 the ramp was demolished. The waterwheel was either scrapped or re-used elsewhere.[11]

Morwellham Quay kilns with site of the stone incline ramp indicated. This was removed after 1873. *Robert Waterhouse*

Excavated turntable by the limekiln quay, dating from 1816, with cast iron edge rails and earlier plate rails. *Robert Waterhouse*

Surviving limekilns and the water-powered ramp serving them to the left, at Newquay.
Robert Waterhouse

designed to defend the neck of land between Whitsand Bay on the English Channel and the Lynher estuary. The forts were built in the period 1859-1860 and a temporary incline formed part of the construction tramway. Between 1886 and 1893 the military railway was established and an incline was built up from the Lynher to Scraesdon Fort near the village of Antony. This was operated as a standard-gauge three-rail cable-worked inclined plane with a passing loop, in all about 1,150 feet long, powered by a stationary steam engine at the summit at Scraesdon. The gradient was 1 in 7 and the plane passed under the entrance to the fort at its head and the A374 road near its foot. At the foot, two turntables served a short section of locomotive-hauled railway which ran out to Wacker Quay. A second loco-hauled line linked Scraesdon with the fort at Tregantle. The railway had a short working life and was out of use by 1903.[13] The incline is now overgrown and inaccesible.

Newquay Limekilns, Gulworthy
SX 45426961

A kiln at Newquay was first constructed in 1812, expanded to a bank of three in 1817. A reconstruction costing £300 occurred in 1825 with a water-powered ramp forming part of the complex. In 1850 the ramp was raised in height. Perry Spear and Company operated this kiln bank from 1854 to 1904; it was then worked intermittently and finally abandoned in 1914. Here the overshot waterwheel was smaller than at Morwellham; 8 foot 6 inches diameter by 3 foot 6 inches and the rail gauge was then 3 foot 6 inches – it may earlier have been a plateway, 4 foot 2 inches gauge. The ramp and kilns are on private land but are reachable on foot from Morwellham Quay.[12]

Scraesdon Incline, Tregantle Military Railway, Antony
SX 39505516 FOOT – SX39425481 HEAD

The Tregantle Military Railway was built to serve forts constructed at Scraesdon and Tregantle, which were

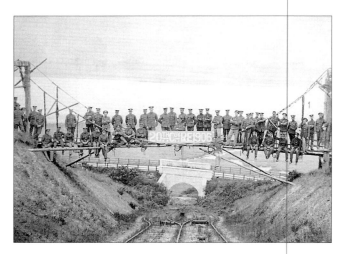

Scraesdon Incline, Tregantle Military Railway. The three-rail track seen during a Royal Engineers exercise in 1906, by which time it had already fallen into disuse.

The Tavistock Canal inclined plane on a shallow embankment. A twentieth century view. *Robert Waterhouse*

Tavistock Limekilns, Tavistock

SX 47987410

A set of kilns once existed at the Tavistock basin of the canal from Morwellham, their ramp worked by an breastshot waterwheel. They were operated by Gill and Rundle from 1817 and provided the model for Hodge's kiln, Moorswater, near Liskeard. The plane or ramp here was about 50 feet long; the waterwheel may have been 16 to 20 foot in diameter. Operations may have ceased in 1873, when the canal closed.[15]

Tavistock Canal – inclined plane to Morwellham Quay, Gulworthy

SX 44417005 HEAD – SX 44476984 FOOT

In 1817 the Tavistock Canal opened via a mile-and-a-half tunnel under Morwell Down to a basin 237 feet above Morwellham Quay on the Tamar. The canal, tunnel and incline were designed by John Taylor (1779–1863). He had arrived in Devon from Norfolk in 1796, and at the age of nineteen ran the Wheal Friendship copper mine at Mary Tavy.

Taylor's canal employed barges. Ores from the mines had to be trans-shipped to special incline wagons at the incline head at the canal's western terminus above the quay. At the quay they would be assayed before shipping to smelters at Swansea, in south Wales. The plane was double-track, 720 feet long with a gradient of 1 in 3 and at the rail gauge was 3 foot 10 inches. Whilst it could be operated by gravity, a 28 foot by 3 foot waterwheel at the incline head was used to haul loaded wagons up from the quay – with typical loads of limestone and culm for a bank of limekilns at Tavistock and lumber for the mines. The wagons were designed to tip their loads and had one set of wheels four inches larger than the other to provide a level platform for the freight; haulage was by chain rather than cable.[14] Sections of the plane are accessible today.

Wheal Crebor, Gulworthy

SX 460724

During construction of the Tavistock canal tunnel under Morwell Down, lodes of copper were discovered, resulting in the development of a mine at its Tavistock end. John Taylor designed an underground incline with its summit at the canal, 20 feet in from the portal. It was probably a plateway.[16] As ores had to be raised rather than lowered, the plane had to be powered. It was worked initially by a 40 foot diameter waterwheel at the incline's head, with canal water acting as a leat. Trucks brought the ore up from the mine. The incline went down 325 feet on a gradient of roughly 1 in 2.[17] Such an arrangement was, it seems, unique in the south west, but it was not entirely original: the Duke of Bridgewater's Worsley Navigable Levels had a twin-tunnel underground canal inclined plane dating from 1797. It was self-acting, a loaded tub boat descending, bringing up an empty one.[18] Nor was a waterwheel working underground a novel concept at this date: Swedish engineer Henric Kalmeter saw one installed on the Marquis mine nearby in 1724.[19] Crebor was a most successful mine, operating from 1807 until 1902.

North and East Cornwall

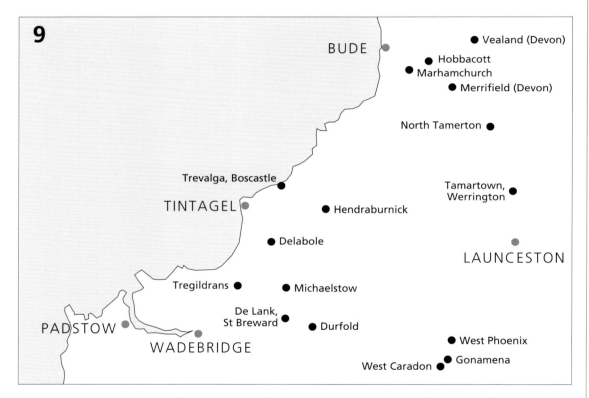

9

Vealand (Devon)

Hobbacott
Marhamchurch
Merrifield (Devon)

BUDE

North Tamerton

Trevalga, Boscastle

Tamartown,
Werrington

TINTAGEL

Hendraburnick

Delabole

LAUNCESTON

Tregildrans

Michaelstow

De Lank,
St Breward

Durfold

PADSTOW

West Phoenix

Gonamena

WADEBRIDGE

West Caradon

The most impressive monument to canal engineering in the south western counties today is arguably the Bude Canal. It featured six inclined planes and was operational from 1825. James Green was its engineer, influenced to some extent by the American inventor, Robert Fulton. North Cornwall also contained the most impressive slate quarry in the south west;

Delabole had no less than nine incline tracks at work in 1906. Planes were also built to access mines and quarries on Bodmin Moor and the surrounding hinterland. Stone from the De Lank Quarry at St Breward went out via two planes and was used to construct lighthouses and harbour works – including docks at Gibraltar and Singapore.

Boscastle Slate Quarry, Trevalga

SX 08109052

A probable inclined plane here: a linear bank on the cliff edge used to haul slate up from the quarry, possibly worked by horse whim.[1]

Bude Canal

Six inclined planes, all water-powered.

Hobbacott Incline, Launcells

SS 24210461 FOOT – SS 24400482 HEAD
935 FEET LONG, RISE 225 FEET.
On the 'Planekeepers Path': walkable. The plane is signed 'Thurlibeer Incline'; listed Grade II.

Marhamchurch Incline, Marhamchurch

SS 21800375 FOOT – SS 22080373 HEAD
836 FEET LONG; RISE 120 FEET.
Foot of incline cleared in 2009.

Merrifield Incline, Bridgerule

SS 27120167 FOOT – SS 27100178 HEAD
360 FEET LONG, RISE 60 FEET.
Wheelpit chamber on private land.

Tamerton Incline, North Tamerton

SX 32479569 FOOT – SX 32979578 HEAD
360 FEET LONG, RISE 59 FEET
Wheelpit collapsed; on private land.
Basins overgrown and ruinous.

Werrington Incline

SX 33779050 FOOT – SX 33839044 HEAD
259 FEET LONG, RISE 51 FEET.
Wheelpit exists on private land.

Vealand Incline, Pancrasweek

SS 28420672 FOOT – SS 28580665 HEAD
500 FEET LONG, RISE 58 FEET.
Track bed in situ; wheelpit filled in.

James Green's Bude Canal scheme, an ambitious design developed in 1817-18, took the waterway over hilly country towards Launceston and Holsworthy and involved no less than six inclined planes, the most impressive being Hobbacott at 935 feet long with a rise of 225 feet and Marhamchurch at 836 feet with a rise of 120 feet. From a summit near Red Post the canal then descended the Tamar valley via Merrifield, Tamerton and Werrington planes. A sixth plane at Vealand

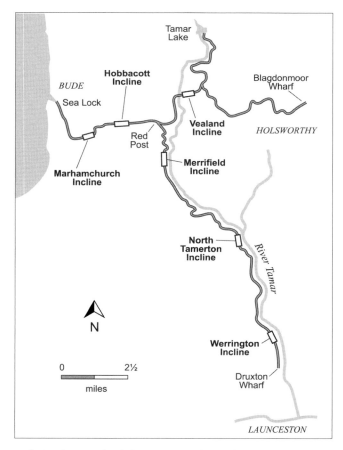

Bude Canal. Two inclined planes were needed to take the canal up to Red Post and then a further three descended down the Tamar valley to Druxton Wharf, near Launceston. A sixth plane at Vealand raised a branch towards Holsworthy and the canal reservoir, now Tamar Lake.

took a branch north-east to Virworthy, to the canal reservoir – now Tamar Lake – and to a wharf at Blagdonmoor, near Holsworthy.

Five of these inclines were powered by overshot waterwheels; at Hobbacott, a bucket in a well was used to draw boats up and this was later supplemented by a steam engine at the incline summit. The planes were all twin track. Wheeled tub-boats obviated the need for trans-shipment at the inclines. There were drawbacks – the wheels tended to damage the canal banks. And technology didn't quite match the concept: the steam engine was often required when the endless chains used in the shafts of the bucket-in-the-well system broke.[2] But

it was an impressive project, built entirely by private finance, and operated from 1825 until 1891, long after the railway age had been established.

The plane manager at Merrifield, Bridgerule, was Abel Yelland, who appears to have settled here in 1847. He was born in Holsworthy in 1819.[3] The underground waterwheel chambers at the head of the canal inclines were dark and dangerous places, with exposed machinery. In October 1858 Yelland met with a fatal accident:

'On the 5th inst. Abel Yelland, who has worked the inclined plane for several years past, at Merrifield, in the parish of Bridgerule on the line of the Bude Canal, was down in the pit

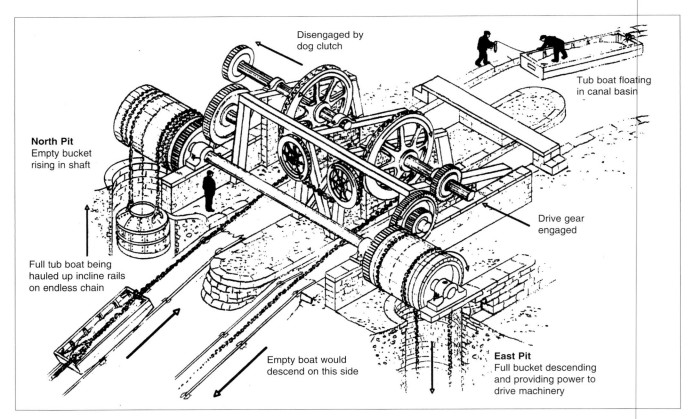

Disengaged by dog clutch

Tub boat floating in canal basin

North Pit
Empty bucket rising in shaft

Drive gear engaged

Full tub boat being hauled up incline rails on endless chain

Empty boat would descend on this side

East Pit
Full bucket descending and providing power to drive machinery

Drawing of the machinery at the summit of the Hobbacott incline, where power was provided by a bucket laden with water descending a well 225 feet deep. *Drawing courtesy B. D. Hughes*

with other workmen, about the machinery (without having taken the precaution to secure the works above) when a boater, coming up with a trip of boats, swelled the water out over the banks, which put the water wheel around and the machinery in motion, by which the unfortunate man's thigh was fearfully crushed. Mr King, of Stratton .. amputated the limb, but from the excessive loss of blood that had taken place, the poor sufferer sank from it. He was a trusty and well disposed man, in the prime of life, and has left a widow and family to lament his untimely death.'[4]

At Hobbacott on midsummer day in 1827 '59 boats were taken over the plane'.[5] At Marhamchurch incline semaphore signals were installed at the foot and summit as a means of communication. One or two barges were carried up at a time; two or three, if empty, were allowed to descend.

De Lank Quarry. The incline linking the quarry with railway from Wenfordbridge to Boscarne Junction. Standard-gauge, three-rail formation. *Locomotive and General Photographs*

De Lank Quarry, St Breward
MAIN INCLINE SX 08607517 FOOT – SX 09087508 HEAD
QUARRY INCLINE SX 102751 FOOT – SX102752 HEAD

Here an incline, half a mile long and with a gradient of 1 in 9, linked the quarry with the terminus of the branch line at Wenford Bridge in the Camel valley. It was probably constructed in 1890 to standard gauge – no trans-shipment was required at Wenford Bridge – and was three-rail throughout, except for the passing loop. Several lighthouses were built with De Lank granite including Smalls, Bishop Rock, Beachy Head and Needles. Stone also went to Putney (1884), Chelsea (1932) and Lambeth (1934) bridges, as well as docks at Gibraltar and Singapore. The incline was in use until 1941. A second, much shorter plane, saw service within the quarry.[6] This was laid as three-rail track above the passing loop and was single track below.

Bude Canal. The two tub boat bays at the foot of the Hobbacott incline. A horizontal return wheel was originally mounted on a vertical shaft located on the island between the two bays, supported by an overhead gantry. The wheel would have carried the continuous chain, to which the tub boats hooked onto, up and down the twin-track incline. *Dave Tonkin*

Below: Delabole Slate Quarry, Delabole. A view down the main six-track incline in 1907. The incline was over 900 foot long with a gradient of 1 in 2½. It was steam powered, but the quarry still used waterwheels which can be seen on the left of this image. *T. Clifford Hall/British Geological Survey*

Delabole Quarry, Delabole, St Teath

SX 07438388 FOOT – SX 07528368 HEAD

Slate has been worked by quarrymen in the south west for several centuries. In Elizabethan times the quarry at Delabole, north Cornwall, was already being exploited for slate.

By 1600 Delabole slate was being exported to the Netherlands, shipped from Port Gaverne and Port Isaac. In the nineteenth century several workings here were merged to form one major quarry. By 1834 a plane worked by a stationary steam engine had been adopted as the main method to haul the slate out of the ever-deepening pit. In

1886 a worker was killed in the quarry when the brake on two descending wagons slipped on a recently constructed incline: the wagons derailed on a point and tipped over into the pit, crushing him. A 3-foot gauge tramway with a four-track incline was replaced by a six-track incline of 2-foot gauge, possibly as early as 1879. This was the year when the management took delivery of 2-foot gauge 'quarry' Hunslet locomotives, to work the lines at surface. The incline was then between 900 feet and 1,000 feet long with a gradient of 1 in 2½ and was powered by three of the seven steam engines on site; by 1906 there were three subsidiary inclines too. Two were at work to the north and north west of the main plane. Steam power was assisted by gravity: two or three empty wagons acted as a counterweight to the loaded wagon being hauled up the incline. There was a signalling system by 1886; details are not known. By the 1970s the quarry was 500 feet deep and the incline was 1,100 feet long and powered by electric motors installed in 1929.[7]

Today the inclines have gone and lorries drive down to the enlarged quarry floor. There is a viewing platform overlooking the pit.

Durfold China Clay Works, Blisland

SX 11477355 FOOT – SX 11307364 HEAD

Durfold was the earliest of the china clay workings on Bodmin Moor, dating from 1864. By 1870 it was under the management of Frank Parkyn, son of a Lerryn wool merchant, and a great advocate of water power. Durfold clayworks were situated in a steep-sided valley below the moor. A narrow-gauge single-track inclined plane was constructed to transport dried clay from the kilns up to the road between Metherin Downs and Blisland. The plane was about 930 feet long with a rise of 115 feet. Loaded wagons were powered up the plane by an overshot waterwheel at its foot; its dimensions about 28 foot by 4 foot 6 inches. Water reached the wheel by a long launder running above the valley floor. Its axle was directly attached to a gear which meshed with a pinion to transfer the drive through 90 degrees. The pinion was on a second axle carrying the winding drum or winch. The haulage cable passed over rollers laid between the rails and was returned on sheaves carried on posts beside the tramway. The system was functioning in the period 1876-1900. There is little evidence of the tramway on the ground today.[8]

Durfold China Clay Works, Bodmin Moor. A narrow-gauge single track inclined plane powered by a 28-foot waterwheel with a winch at its foot. The haulage cable runs out to the head of the incline on sheaves mounted on poles. *Wheal Martyn China Clay Museum*

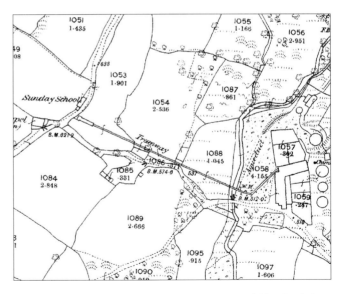

Durfold China Clay Works, Blisland, Bodmin Moor. Durfold inclined plane in 1882. *Old-Maps*

Durfold was the site where Frank Parkyn installed a third-hand 50-foot diameter waterwheel to pump pits at Temple 2½ miles away. It was soon replaced by electric pumps and is now restored as a tourist attraction at Snafell in the Isle of Man, where it had worked before.

Gonamena incline, Liskeard and Caradon Railway, Minions, Linkinhorne
SX 26307030 FOOT – SX 26137052 HEAD

Construction began on the standard-gauge Liskeard and Caradon Railway in 1844 at the Cheeswring and part of the line opened, to Tremabe, later that year. It linked the copper mines at Caradon and, via the Gonamena incline, Cheeswring granite quarry with the Liskeard and Looe Canal at Moorswater, near Liskeard. The line opened through to the canal in 1846. No detail of the incline's operation survives: it

Gonamena inclined plane, Liskeard and Caradon Railway. Stone blocks remain in 2011. The cutting was wide enough for twin tracks. Looking towards Minions. *Robin Whalley*

was double track and was self-acting with a gradient of 1 in 11. Wagons worked over it typically had a capacity of six tons, carrying ores and granite to Moorswater and Looe, and Welsh coal for the Cornish steam engines on the mines around Minions. The plane employed ropes which were renewed every eight or nine years. By 1873 the incline had been bypassed; its track lifted by 1882. The formation survives today and is accessible from the summit but not from the foot of the incline.[9]

Hendraburnick Quarry, Davidstow
SX 141877

The site is by Higher Trehane Farm, on the A39 Camelford-Bude highway. It was a relatively small working in 1962 and the site was disused by 1978. Michael Messenger has noted one, possibly two, inclined planes linking the now flooded workings.[10]

Long Grass and Gillow Quarries, Tintagel
LONG GRASS QUARRY SX 04708821 – SX 04758825 HEAD
GILLOW QUARRY SX 04848860 FOOT – SX 04878857 HEAD

Two cliff-edge slate quarries. Long Grass inclined plane was constructed after 1884 and is shown on the 1907 1:2,500 Ordnance Survey map. It ran from dressing floors to the cliff-top where a whim provided power. The Gillow Quarry plane is ill-defined and does not appear on any early large scale maps.[11]

Michaelstow Quarry, Michaelstow
SX 08847907

This was a twentieth century excavation: the quarry did not exist in 1907. It served Cornwall Council. An inclined plane was noted in 1969, by which time the workings were disused. The quarry was mostly worked by hand but the short inclined plane had its own winding engine. The plant had been cleared by the summer of 1970.[12]

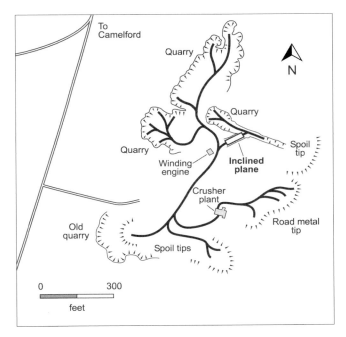

Michaelstow Quarry. The location of the inclined plane and approximate layout of the internal tramways in the 1960s.

Tregildrans, Pendoggett, St Kew
SX 036793

The elvan quarry at Tregildrans was in full production following World War I. It was established by Leonard Tom, near the railway line to Padstow – the concept had come to him in a dream. Here a crusher plant was installed alongside standard gauge sidings and the rock was brought up to it by a 900-foot-long inclined plane from the quarry pit. This narrow-gauge single-track incline was powered by a stationary Ruston and Hornsby steam engine. In later years twin Blackstone diesel engines hauled the wagons to the crusher and also worked all the other machinery in the quarry. A signalling system was operated by a bell boy in the quarry pit. When a wagon was ready to be raised to ground level, the boy tugged a rope that rang a bell in the engine house, where the operator engaged the diesel engines with the drum at the incline head. Airfields at Davidstow and St

Eval and breakwaters at Port Isaac were some of the destinations for the quarried stone. The single-track incline ceased work in 1956.[13]

West Caradon Mine, Minions, Linkinhorne
SX 263697 FOOT – SX263698 HEAD

On Bodmin Moor the copper mine at West Caradon was linked to the Liskeard and Caradon Railway by a 480-foot-long standard-gauge inclined plane, with a gradient of 1 in 6. It joined the Cheesewring branch a little below that line's Gonamena incline, near Crow's Nest.[14]

West Phoenix Mine, Minions, Linkinhorne
SX 26507220 FOOT – SX 26117219 HEAD

A narrow gauge tramway on an inclined plane was constructed to link Phoenix United with West Phoenix Mine at some time after 1870. It burrowed under the Kilmar Railway and near its summit ran in cutting; terminating near Stowe's Shaft. The plane was probably self-acting, taking ore down to Phoenix United for processing.[15] Its total length was about 1,230 feet.

The head of the West Phoenix tramway incline. *Bob Acton*

Mid Cornwall

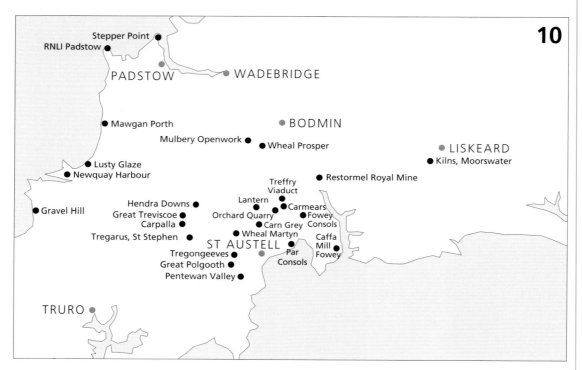

10

Stepper Point
RNLI Padstow
PADSTOW ● WADEBRIDGE
● Mawgan Porth ● BODMIN
Mulbery Openwork ● ● Wheal Prosper ● LISKEARD
● Kilns, Moorswater
● Lusty Glaze
● Newquay Harbour ● Restormel Royal Mine
Treffry
● Gravel Hill Viaduct
Lantern
Hendra Downs ● Carmears
Great Treviscoe ● Orchard Quarry ● Fowey
Carpalla ● Carn Grey Consols
Tregarus, St Stephen ● ● Wheal Martyn Caffa
ST AUSTELL Mill
Tregongeeves ● Par Fowey
Great Polgooth ● Consols
Pentewan Valley ●
TRURO ●

Cable-worked planes in Mid Cornwall were employed in mining, quarrying and in the development of the china clay industry. J. T. Treffry of Fowey was the district's leading light in the early Victorian era. Like John Taylor he was a keen exponent of water powered planes. He is known to have planned at least eight planes in the country between Fowey and Newquay.[1]

Earlier, in 1773, John Edyvean's St Columb Canal featured two primitive inclined planes on coastal cliffs near Newquay.

A more sophisticated example was in use at Happy Union tin mine, near St Austell, by 1783. This site is now lost.

By 1914 over 150 china clay works were in production. It is not the intention here to enumerate the various sites, many of which have since been much enlarged, using modern extractive methods, and have lost their inclines and sky tips. The industry has been recorded elsewhere; one or two sample planes are noted here.[2]

Caffa Mill Pill – Penventinue, Fowey
SX 12575228 FOOT – SX 11685336 HEAD

At Caffa Mill, Fowey, where J. T. Treffry owned limekilns and a shipbuilding yard, a waterwheel situated at the foot of an incline was used to haul wagons taking lime, manure and sea sand up to his farm at Penventinue. The incline, built circa 1844, was about 870 feet long on a gradient of 1 in 3 and the rail track gauge was about 3 foot; the track appears to have been laid as three-rail, with a passing loop at halfway. It was still functioning in 1851. It has been suggested that it was originally intended as part of a tramway linking Fowey Consols with Fowey harbour, and apparently some copper ore was sent down it. In the event, Treffry decided to develop a new harbour at Par instead.[3] The line of the formation is visible in field boundaries.

Carmears Incline, Luxulyan valley, Lanlivery
SX 07145627 FOOT – SX 06625668 HEAD

The Carmears inclined plane linked the upper level of the Treffry tramway with Ponts Mill, and was part of a system carrying granite, china clay and minerals to J. T. Treffry's Par harbour via the three-mile-long Par Canal. The standard-gauge incline was recorded as 2,871 feet long in 1844. It has a gradient ranging from 1 in 8 to 1 in 12 and was worked by a 30 foot by 8 foot 6 inch waterwheel at its head, generating 76 horse power. This wheel could haul 30 tons up the incline in 10 minutes. Its leat, brought over the Treffry viaduct, built 1839-42, still runs. The incline lifted wagons 325 feet, which were then horse-drawn over the viaduct. Wire rope was used for haulage, which must have been one of its earliest applications in the south west. Carmears functioned until 1874. The incline is accessible today.[4]

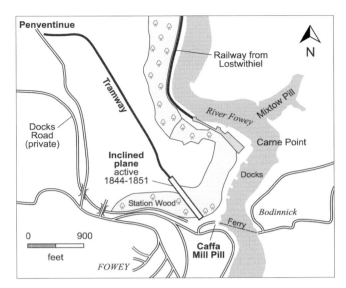

Remains of the water-powered incline from Caffamill to Penventinue can be seen on the eastern edge of Station Wood, Fowey, a National Trust property. The tramway on the plateau above was probably worked by horses.

Carmears incline, Luxulyan valley. This was once powered by a 30 foot by 8½ foot waterwheel, fed by a leat brought across the Treffry viaduct. *Miocene*

Carn Grey Quarries Tramway, Trethurgy, St Austell

SX 03375509

Two quarries were served by narrow-gauge inclines; a third 18-inch tramway worked over an incline to a loading point. The tramway system was active in 1933 but by 1971 the quarry floors had flooded.[5]

Carpalla Tramway, St Stephen-in-Brannel

SW 963544 HEAD. GWR BRANCH SIDINGS
SW 962541 MIDPOINT. ENGINE HOUSE/DRIVE WINCHES
SW 962539 FOOT. CARPALLA KILNS

The Carpalla china clay kilns were linked by a tramway that ran up to a loading wharf on the Great Western's branch line south of Drinnick Mill. It was operated as an inclined plane, worked as two sections: Carpalla kilns-Penbough and Penbough-GWR sidings. Winding drums were located at Penbough, by an engine house which may have been the power source. The tramway functioned from 1898 to 1942. It is clearly visible on the 1932 Ordnance Survey 1:2,500 of the area. Total length was about 1,950 feet with a rise of 137 feet. The derelict drums and associated gear were still on site when

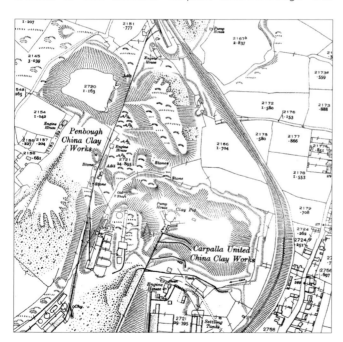

The Carpalla Tramway in 1932. Two inclined planes were worked, either side of the summit at Penbough. Sweeping round to the east is the GWR's St Dennis branch line. *Old-Maps*

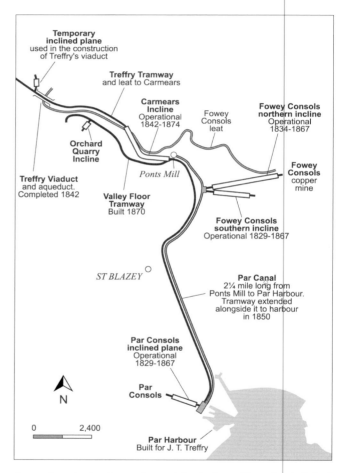

Fowey Consols, Luxulyan valley and Par harbour. The valley is full of interesting industrial archaeological sites: at this scale the present Par-Newquay railway has been omitted for the sake of clarity. Six cable-worked inclined planes are shown here. Five of these, together with Par harbour and canal, the Treffry viaduct and tramway, were built for J. T. Treffry.

seen by Maurice Dart in 1963.[6] The tramway's formation is now partly lost under a mica dam and associated china clay works.

Fowey Consols, near St Blazey, Tywardreath and Par
SOUTHERN INCLINE
SX 07555580 FOOT – SX07855580 HEAD
NORTHERN INCLINE
SX 07555581 FOOT – SX 083558 HEAD

This was one of J. T. Treffry's major projects, providing much of his wealth, enabling him to finance many other schemes. Here the earlier and shorter incline, 1,127 feet long, was self-acting, taking copper ores from the mine down to the canal, including a short tunnel under the St Blazey-Lostwithiel road. The second incline, 2,640 feet long, including an 840-foot tunnel, was worked by a 30 horse-power waterwheel at the incline head, powered by a leat brought down from Molinnis, four miles away. It was used to haul materials such as coal to the mine and could raise a 10-ton load up 280 feet in 15 minutes.[7] These inclines worked into the late 1860s. Their course has largely been lost today: a bridge abutment at SX 077558 indicates the route of the second incline where it crossed over a minor road and the sites of the lower portals of both tunnels are visible.

Gravel Hill Mine, Perranzabuloe
BEACH INCLINED PLANE
SW 76385747 FOOT – SW 76595729 HEAD

This iron mine was at work in 1860. The main adit was at the north end of Perran Beach, below the dunes on Penhale Sands. By 1874 a stationary steam engine, also used for pumping the mine, had been installed to haul ore up an 180-foot inclined plane to the tramway summit. A second plane with a 'self-acting drum' lowered wagons eastwards to a siding on the Cornwall Mineral Railway, where the iron ore was transferred into railway trucks. The mine closed in 1884 and the track from Treamble was lifted in 1888.[8]

Great Polgooth Mine, St Mewan/St Ewe
SX 999505 FOOT, STAMPS ENGINE

An inclined plane was in use here by 1823. The tramway ran from the stamps house to the top of Mulvra Hill and was partly in cutting. The area had been worked for tin for over a century and by 1837 Polgooth was one of the county's major producers of tin. In 1881 the mine was disused. A new stamps engine house was built at the foot of the incline in 1882; all mining had ceased by 1900.[9]

Great Treviscoe Clay Works, St Dennis
SW 940560 foot – SW 94105595 head

A narrow-gauge inclined plane linked Great Treviscoe siding on the St Dennis branch with Great Treviscoe kiln. It appears to have been single track, about 3 foot gauge, on stone sleeper blocks that may have been re-cycled from one of J. T. Treffry's tramways.[10]

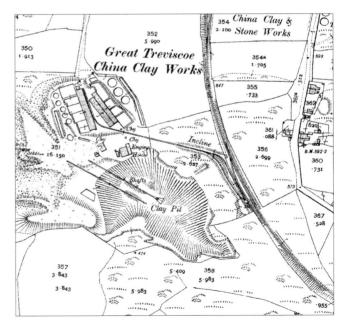

Great Treviscoe China Clay Works in 1907, with its incline to the GWR's St Dennis branch line extant. *Old-Maps*

Happy Union Tin Mine, Pentewan valley
LOCATION NOT NOW KNOWN

At Happy Union in the Pentewan valley, south of St Austell, a tin mine was, by 1783, equipped with a twin-track inclined plane worked by a large horse whim to raise the 'tin ground' from its floor. China clay producers would have witnessed this technology and it came to be adopted in their pits.[11]

As the pits grew deeper, steam power was employed. Cornish beam engines, of the type used in tin and copper mines, were introduced to pump china clay slurry from the pits and to haul the skips taking stent to the sky tips that became such a feature of mid Cornwall in the twentieth century.

Derelict engine house on Hendra Downs in the 1940s. It once powered the incline from Gullies Wharf, St Dennis and pumped Hendra Old Pit. *Wheal Martyn China Clay Museum*

Happy Union Tin Mine, near St Austell, 1783. The illustration, published anonymously in Berlin in 1790, is thought to be by Rudolf Erich Raspe. Raspe referred to an underground railway here, although this illustration implies an openwork. It shows two features later adopted by the china clay industry. A] The twin-track inclined plane, worked by a horse gin or whim. B] A waterwheel powered pump linked to the pit floor by an adit. The mine, in the Pentewan valley, was begun in 1780 and closed in 1837.
C. M. Bristow

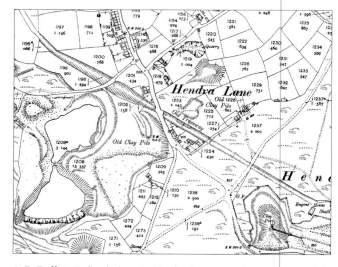

J. T. Treffry's inclined plane to Hendra Downs, to the south east of St Dennis village, was marked 'Old Tramway' on the 1907 Ordnance Survey map; its track lifted at least 27 years earlier. The engine house at the top of the incline can be seen; it also served the adjoining china clay pit. Much of the formation has been lost in more recent years. *Old-Maps*

Hendra Downs Tramway, St Dennis
SW 949572 FOOT – SW 954569 HEAD

This incline linked clay pits on Hendra Downs with Treffry's railway to Newquay at Gullies Wharf, which had opened in 1849. It was powered by a beam engine which also served the clayworks, although the incline had priority. The plane may have been operational by 1852 and was in use in 1857.[12] Coal was imported from Newquay harbour for the china clay dries and the beam engine; china clay and stone from Quarry Close were shipped out.[13] The incline passed just to the north east of Parkandillack clay works, disused by 1907. Its track had already been lifted by 1881.[14] The formation at the foot of the plane was still evident 20 years ago and the beam engine house was said to be extant in 1970, although the upper part of the route was lost as the clay pit was extended.

Lantern China Clay Pit, near Rescorla, Bugle
SX 02505704

Lantern pit is included here as it was typical of many china clay works in the St Austell area and elements of the site have survived, although now much overgrown. A steam engine worked the pumps in the adit and also powered the steel cable used to haul the trucks from the pit floor to the dumps on the single-track inclined plane. Established in 1858, the pit closed in 1942. The incline plane has gone: its pit was flooded by 1971.[15]

Limekilns at Moorswater, near Liskeard
WILLIAM HODGE'S LIMEKILN
SX 23596414
JOHN LYNE'S LIMEKILNS
SX 23756410

William Chapell Hodge's limekiln was built at Moorswater, at the head of the canal from Looe harbour. It was under construction in 1828. Hodge was a banker and landed proprietor of Plymouth. His two-pot structure was modelled on the now lost water-powered kilns at Tavistock canal basin. The single-track plane – it carried a plateway of 2 foot 6 inch gauge, which led from the canal basin – was built on pillars, and has since been removed. It was powered by an undershot

Lantern China Clay Pit with steam-powered incline to sky tip. In operation in 1905. *T. C. Hall/British Geological Survey*

Stent about to be tipped from wagon to skip at foot of incline to sky tip. *Wheal Martyn China Clay Museum*

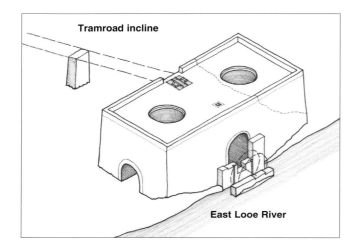

Tramroad incline

East Looe River

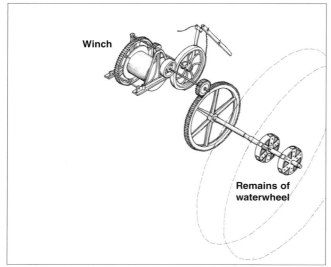

Winch

Remains of waterwheel

Hodges Kiln, Moorswater, Liskeard. With the now-vanished inclined plane and the water-powered gearing to provide haulage on it.
Drawing courtesy of Martin Watts

waterwheel. A plateway turntable, used to transfer a wagon from the incline to one of the kiln pots, was still extant in this century, together with the incline winch and part of the brake and the waterwheel axle and hubs.[16]

On the other side of the basin John Lyne owned two banks of kilns, five in total, in 1842. These were built circa 1831. They were served by a inclined plane, extant in 1851-1857 and worked by an overshot waterwheel, fed by a culvert from a pond to the north.

In 1855 they had come into the hands of Hopkins & Co and were being run by J. C. Isaac, a Liskeard merchant. The waterwheel and tramway were not shown on the Ordnance Survey map of 1887, but the kilns remained in use until early in the twentieth century: by 1910 lime was available by rail, direct from Plymouth quarries.[17] A third Cornish kiln site with inclined plane was indicated on a plan of Devoran Wharf, near Truro, in 1832. All trace of this single pot kiln and its near neighbours has gone.[18]

Mulberry Open Work, Lanivet, near Bodmin
SX 015659

Mulberry Hill tin mine was an opencast working which produced 1,350 tons of tin between 1859 and 1916. The site featured two narrow gauge tramways; that from the higher Shallow Adit ran down to the stamps and dressing floors on an incline, to the west.[19]

Newquay Harbour, Newquay
SW 808619 FOOT – SW 807618 HEAD

J. T. Treffry intended to link his port of Par on the south coast with Newquay on the north coast by tramway. He had acquired Newquay harbour in 1836 but it was not until after his death in 1850 that a through route was completed. A branch to his china clay pit at Hendra was opened in 1852; another branch ran to East Wheal Rose lead mine near Newlyn East. At Newquay the main line from Roche, worked by horses, descended to the port through a tunnel. Here cable working took over: the tunnel incline had a gradient of 1 in 4½. A steam winding engine was installed at the incline head. Newquay ceased to function as a commercial port in 1922; rail traffic to the quays followed suit in 1926. The tunnel is now sealed.[20]

Newquay. The single-track standard-gauge incline descending through a tunnel to the harbour. Seen in 1926. *Michael Messenger Collection*

Orchard Granite Quarry, Luxulyan valley, Luxulyan
SX 06155675

A short inclined plane was required to link the quarry workings on the hillslope with the Rock Mills Quarry Tramway in the valley below. Here it crossed the Luxulyan river on a granite slab bridge. Constructed in 1867-1870 by the South Cornwall Granite Co, the tramway linked Rock and Orchard Quarries to Pontsmill. The formation of the incline was visible in 1987 but the power source was not identified: it is probable that the plane was worked by gravity.[21]

Par Consols, St Blazey
SX 07485300 FOOT – SX 07025309 HEAD

This inclined plane was a project developed by J. T. Treffry and his agent William Pease. It was completed in 1841 and took ore from his mine above Par to his port. It was about 870 feet long with a rise of about 130 feet on a gradient of 1 in 7. The tramway functioned from 1841 to 1869; the track had been lifted by 1881 and its course, even then, was not entirely clear. Power was provided by a 14-inch stationary steam engine, as unlike the situation at Fowey Consols, Treffry was unable to bring a leat to the mine. While much of the incline's work was done by gravity, the steam engine was used to bring coal up from Par docks, to provide power for the other engines at work on the mine. It also worked a sawmill. Mine output included 122,689 tons of copper, 3,785 tons of tin and some zinc. Par Consols employed over 700 people in 1844.[22] Today the mine site is very overgrown and the course of the incline has largely been lost under later developments.

Restormel Royal Iron Mine, Lostwithiel
Three inclines

BARNGATE LEVEL
SX 10176148 FOOT– SX 10066136 HEAD
CHURCHPARK WOOD
SX 10406069 FOOT – SX 10236080 HEAD
SOUTH RESTORMEL
SX 10336054 FOOT – SX 10186047 HEAD

This sett was at work in 1797, when known as Trinity Mine. It was to become the most successful iron mine in Cornwall and during its working life as many as three inclined planes may have been employed. It was a linear working running roughly north-south, with some openworks and three underground levels. Barngate Level was the highest and from this level an inclined plane descended overground to the north west of Restormel Castle. The middle level was known as Watergate and ore was hauled out by horses on a tramway which ran from an adit to the north west of the Barngate incline, and then wound round below Restormel Castle to Churchpark Wood. Here it is thought was a second incline to take the tramway down to the lane by the river Fowey. A little further on was the adit to the lowest level in the mine – Taylor's Level. A smithy stood nearby. A horse-drawn tramway then ran down through the streets of Lostwithiel and to quays on the Fowey at SX 10455940, where the ore was shipped. The tramway operated throughout in 1838.

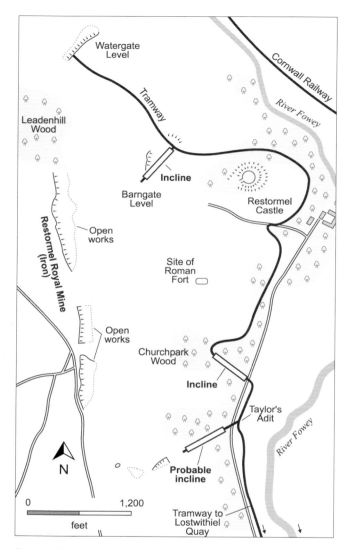

Restormel Royal Iron Mine, Lostwithiel, with the sites of three inclined planes shown. The third was buit in 1874. The tramway route is from the mine plan of 1849.

One incline was at work in 1837; it was probably the presumed plane at Churchpark Wood:[23]

'St Austell. On the 5th inst, a powerful machine was set to work on the inclined plane and railroad at Restormel Mine, near Lostwithiel, which is carried on with great spirit under A. Thompson Esq. Much praise is due to Mr T. Geach, of St Austell, under whose superintendence the engine was erected; and its use will enhance the profits of the enterprising adventurers of this very productive mine, which is the richest iron mine in Cornwall ..' [24]

It was possibly at this location that a fatality occurred in 1839: 'Fatal accident at Lostwithiel. On Wednesday last as two men, employed to attend the waggons at the bottom of the iron mine in this place, were engaged in their usual work, a waggon in the course of its descent became disengaged and one of the men called Hicks, who had lately come from the west, seeing it coming down at a rapid rate, got to one side of the tram to avoid the danger; but the waggon when it came opposite him bounded off its course and crushed him to death in an instant. The poor fellow has left a wife and five children. The other man escaped unhurt.' [25]

Queen Victoria and Prince Albert visited the mine in 1846. 127,796 tons of iron ore were raised between 1855 and 1883. From 1852-1873 the sett was owned by John Taylor & Sons, on lease from the Duchy of Cornwall, and the Restormel Iron Mining Company managed the mine from 1874. A further lode of ore was discovered at the beginning of that year, to the south west of Taylor's adit, at a site also known as South Restormel. A new tramway on an inclined plane was run up the steep-sided valley. It took ore from the new lode down to a point close to Taylor's adit and is shown on the 1:2,500 Ordnance Survey map for 1881. The mine closed in 1883. It briefly re-opened between 1908 and 1910. The Barngate and 1874 inclines have vanished and the only traces of the tramway are still visible in Churchpark Wood and to the south of Restormel Castle.[26]

At Churchpark Wood the formation of the inclined plane has survived in part. It can been seen as a cutting, apparently backfilled by its summit; the site remains in woodland: the upper section is not readily identifiable.

Rack-and-pinion inclined plane serving the new RNLI Padstow lifeboat station at Mother Ivey's Bay. *Simon Burgess/PBWC Architects*

RNLI Padstow Lifeboat Station, Mother Ivey's Bay, St Merryn
SW 860765

Padstow RNLI lifeboat station has been located at Mother Ivey's Bay near Trevone since 1967, where deep water access is available at all states of the tide. Here a 106-foot long cable-operated single-track inclined plane was constructed, linking the cliff top and the station. It was altered in 2008-9 to adapt to the new, award-winning lifeboat station designed by PBWC Architects of St Ives. Cable operation has gone; instead this is now a rack-and-pinion cliff lift, powered by a 750 kW electric

motor, the only such cliff lift in the south west. It has a gradient a little steeper than 1 in 1. As at the Lizard, where a similar, cable-operated, plane exists, the lift is used as access by lifeboatmen, for raising casualties and for delivering supplies and equipment. This is a private facility but viewable from the cliff top.

St Columb Canal, Newquay and Mawgan-in-Pydar
SW 82426255 LUSTY GLAZE; SW 8467 MAWGAN PORTH

In 1773 John Edyvean planned a semi-circular canal running via St Columb to terminii above beaches at Mawgan Porth and Lusty Glaze, Newquay. Sand and seaweed – used as fertilizer – were to be hauled up to the canal in boxes over plank-lined ramps laid down the cliffs. These were operated by horse gins. Edyvean spent his fortune but the canal was never completed, and its inclines could not be described as self-acting.[27]

St Columb Canal. The channel for the plane in the cliff at Lusty Glaze, Newquay, cut in circa 1777. *Lee Andrews*

The Treffry Viaduct was also an aqueduct, its water used to power the Carmears Incline (qv) and augment the Fowey Consols leat. A temporary incline was also used in its construction, running up from T22 through T21 on the plan. *Rosie Spooner (photo). Cornwall Council (plan – for a full credit for this image see the acknowledgements page)*

Stepper Point Quarry, Padstow
SW 91457828

An elvan – elvan is a west country term for greenstone, a rock similar to basalt – quarry was opened at Stepper Point, a remote and inaccessible location, north west of Padstow, soon after World War I. The site included a tramway with an inclined plane at 2-foot gauge and a crusher plant. The tramway ran southwards from the quarry towards an engine house near the The Narrows, on the Camel Estuary. Crushed stone was shipped away by sea. A subsidiary of Amalgamated Roadstone Corporation operated here until closure in 1948.[28]

Treffry Viaduct, Luxulyan valley, Lanlivery
SX 05615739 FOOT – SX 05615729 HEAD

In 1987 a previously undiscovered inclined plane came to light when the Cornwall Archaeological Unit undertook an assessment of industrial and other sites in the Luxulyan valley. It appears that a temporary tramway was used in the construction of the 650-foot long, 100-foot high viaduct which was completed in 1844. The tramway ran on the western side of the valley and headed north before reaching level ground. It terminated at a point level with the top of the viaduct: evidence of an inclined plane descending to a river crossing was found amidst the dense vegetation on the steep valley side.[29]

Tregargus China Stone Mills and inclines
St Stephen-in-Brannel
SW 949540

At Tregargus a system of narrow-gauge tracks with four inclines linked the quarry and six water-powered china stone mills, five working successively off the same leat. The rail gauge was 2-foot and the single-track inclines were relatively

Tregargus China Stone Works, St Stephen in Brannel. One of the four inclined planes linking sections of the tramway system. *Michael Messenger*

Wheal Martyn, Treverbyn, near St Austell
SX 005545

A short replica incline section demonstrates the use of such planes in the china clay industry. It can be seen at the Wheal Martyn China Clay Museum and Country Park. This is open to the public.

Wheal Prosper, Lanivet, Bodmin
SX 035644 FOOT – SX 034643 HEAD

Wheal Prosper was a series of four opencast mines worked for tin from 1846 to 1910, although the mine was shown as disused in 1881. By 1870 ore was taken from the bottom of the workings on a tramway through an adit and down an inclined plane to the stamps and dressing floors situated to the north-east. The tramway was 1,980 feet long with 1,110 feet or so underground. On the surface the tramway was perhaps 870 feet long, with half that length on an inclined plane, descending 62 feet, probably by gravity. During a brief boom in 1870-1872, the mine sold 82 tons of black tin.[32]

short. Installed during the last decade of the nineteenth century, the complex, run by Thomas Olver & Co, ceased operations in 1965.[30] Access is not easy now: the complex is rather overgrown. In recent years a charity, the Tregargus Trust, has been established to conserve and protect the former mills and other structures in the Tregargus valley.

Tregongeeves Quarry, St Ewe
SX 000514

The site is to the south of St Mewan, just within St Ewe parish. *'A 2 ft gauge tramway, with inclines to two roadstone quarries, operated here from 1931-1961…'* The 1933 Ordnance Survey 1:2,500 map shows a tramway running round the edge of one quarry with a line descending into the workings; a second incline is possible in a development to the south east. A diagram of the quarry layout in 1958 shows that one of the inclines was cable worked. The workings have since been backfilled and are now used as a highways depot.[31]

Replica incline at Wheal Martyn china clay museum, The inclines were used to take over-burden, or stent, from the pit to a sky tip, where the wagon would be unloaded automatically. The wagon is shown just above the 'dog hole' or loading bay on the pit floor.

West Cornwall

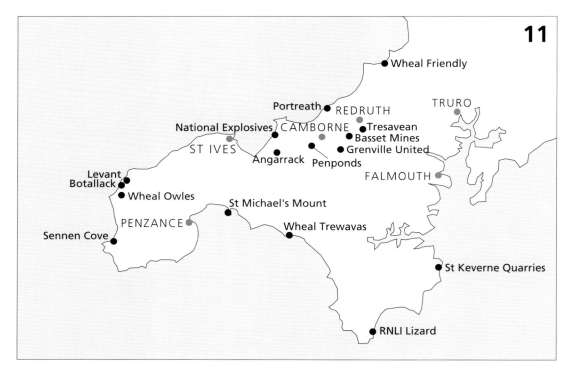

11

Wheal Friendly

TRURO

Portreath • REDRUTH

National Explosives / CAMBORNE • Tresavean
• Basset Mines

ST IVES Grenville United

Angarrack Penponds

FALMOUTH

Levant
Botallack

• Wheal Owles

St Michael's Mount

PENZANCE

Sennen Cove

Wheal Trewavas

St Keverne Quarries

RNLI Lizard

This was mining country and it features some dramatically sited projects such as the Botallack Mine, regarded by a mining authority, writing in 1865, as *'probably the most remarkable in the world'*. Its inclined plane was largely tunnelled through rock, serving workings out under the Atlantic. In addition, construction of the two engine houses on cliff ledges almost certainly required temporary inclined planes from the cliff top, calling for engineering skills of a high order. The Hayle Railway connected the mines of Redruth and Camborne with harbours at Hayle and Portreath. Two of its four inclined planes, completed in 1837, were bypassed when the West Cornwall Railway opened from Truro to Penzance in 1852. A quarry, a lifeboat station and two private inclines are also listed in this section.

Basset Mines, Carn Brea, Redruth

SW 68754019 HEAD OF INCLINE AT WEST BASSET
SW 68973980 HEAD OF INCLINE AT EAST BASSET

At Carn Brea, near Redruth, a group of setts were amalgamated in 1896 to form Basset Mines. A valley ran between steam-powered ore stamps at West Basset and East Basset. The two sites were connected by a 1 foot 8 inch gauge tramway which worked over inclined planes either side of the valley. The mines closed in 1918.[1]

Botallack Mine, St Just in Penwith

SW 36203353 THE CROWNS

In some locations mine shafts were sited on steep sloping ground, as for instance the Botallack Mine's spectacular Crowns section on the coast, in St Just in Penwith. At the Crowns the Boscawen Diagonal Shaft, a single track inclined plane, was constructed from Pearce's Whim – the higher of the two engine houses surviving here – through rock to 1,860 feet below sea level. It was designed by Captain John Rowe, the mine's engineer, and had a tramway of 2 foot 7½ inch gauge. It functioned from 1862 to 1875. There was a disastrous accident in 1863 when eight men and a boy riding on the 'gig' or wagon were killed when the chain on the incline broke. In subsequent operations wire rope replaced the chain. The surface section of the plane was on trestle. Pearce's Whim engine hauled the single wagon; beneath the trestle was an ore bin into which the rock was discharged. A skip then took the rock almost vertically up the cliff on a trestle, to a set of stamps on the hill above, hauled by a second steam engine – The Crowns Whim. A lithograph of 1823 suggests how earlier mining was conducted here. It shows a horse-whim on the cliff top raising a kibble from a shaft on a wooden trestle incline.

By 1878 a tramway ran along the top of the cliffs, linking sections of the mine with a further set of stamps to the south. Two more inclines appear to be indicated, one just north of the Crowns, and a second further south, running down the cliff to a shaft at Wheal Hazard. It was perhaps on one of these planes where, in 1872, a wagon ran away in a gale 'on the tram-road above the 'Crowns'' and dashed down a steep incline, crashing into a small shed and injuring three women, one seriously. Botallack produced tin and copper ores and some arsenic. It was abandoned in 1895. By 1908 much of the sett had been cleared.[2] The mine site was acquired by the National Trust in 2000. It is open to the public.

Botallack Mine, the Crowns section. Top of the Boscawen surface section of the inclined plane/shaft by Pearce's Whim. The wooden trestle, or plane, was taken down after 1875. *Royal Institution of Cornwall*

Grenville United Mines, near Troon, Camborne
SW 66703858 FOOT, STAMPS ENGINE
SW 66783887 HEAD, BY FORTESCUE'S ENGINE HOUSE

Wheal Grenville began productive mining for tin and copper in the 1850s, at which time the South and East mines were worked independently. Wheal Grenville became part of Grenville United in 1906, merging with South Condurrow. The stamps engine to the south was built in 1891 and engines were installed in houses at Fortescue's shaft, East Grenville, on Newton Moor, in 1892. A crusher station here was then linked by a cable-worked inclined tramway up to the stamps, probably worked by steam power. The incline section was about 780 feet long with a rise of 75 feet up from the moor. Grenville United closed in 1921 and the tramway has totally disappeared: it was built on a timber trestle for much of its length. Public footpaths run past its foot and the summit; the late nineteenth century engine houses remain.[3]

Grenville United. The head of the incline tramway by Fortescue's Shaft, Newton Moor, Camborne; seen in the early twentieth century. The engine house still stands but the incline has gone. *Royal Institution of Cornwall*

Hayle Railway
FOUR INCLINED PLANES.

Angarrack Incline, Hayle
SW 581384 FOOT – SW 58743852 HEAD
1,900 feet long, rise 185 feet, approximately.
It was powered by a stationary steam engine at its summit; its enclosure remains but has been built on.

Penponds Incline, Camborne
SW 63833919 - CENTRE OF INCLINE
About 1,900 feet long. The formation by the head of the incline is now largely obscured by housing.

Portreath Incline, Portreath
SW 65734526 FOOT – SW 65774468 HEAD
1,716 feet long with a rise of approximately 240 feet.
Worked by a stationary steam engine.
A cutting survives in cliff; it is used as rough trackway.
Bungalows have invaded the engine house site. The plane is inaccesible at foot – walled off and overgrown; but the embanked lower section is Listed; it forms part of the Portreath Harbour World Heritage Site.

Tresavean Incline, Redruth
SW69394160 FOOT – SW69794078 HEAD
2,640 feet long with a rise of 170 feet.
Worked by gravity.
In operation 1837-1935.
The lower section of the plane has been backfilled but nearer the summit the formation can still be traced.

The Hayle Railway opened in 1837. This standard-gauge line linked the copper mines at Camborne and Redruth with major foundries and shipping quays at Hayle: its prime function was freight. Passengers were carried from 1843. The most well known of the four inclines is the one running down to the harbour at Portreath, a shipping place for copper ores which were to be smelted in Swansea, south Wales. Welsh coal was hauled up the incline to power Cornish engines on the mines. It has a gradient of 1 in 7.
Angarrack and Portreath were each worked by a stationary steam engine at the summit. An 1836 estimate for four

stationary steam engines, with ropes and machinery, amounted to £7,100. In the event the inclines at Penponds and Tresavean were operated by gravity.[4]

The planes were twin track and a contemporary report confirms that the Penponds incline was worked on the counterbalanced principle. Working over the Penponds and Angarrack planes meant that the 9½ mile journey from Redruth to Hayle took 75 minutes in 1843: carriages were lowered down the planes *'made fast to a stout rope'*.

In 1846 a coupling broke on a train loaded with holidaymakers and four carriages with 130 on board dashed down Angarrack incline at great speed. A few souls panicked and jumped off; two were seriously injured, but the runaways eventually came to a safe halt on the line at Hayle Bridge, 2½ miles away.[5]

The West Cornwall Railway took over the concern and realigned the route between Redruth and Hayle, so that by 1852 the inclines at Penponds and Angarrack were bypassed and redundant. The impressive Portreath incline, cut through rock, remained in use until 1932.[6]

Joseph Rogers operated this incline for at least thirty years, from 1871-1901, variously described as 'engineer', 'engine driver' or 'stationary engine driver' in the census returns for Illogan parish. He was a local man, 70 in 1901, and son of another engine driver.[7]

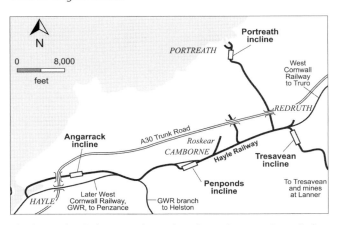

The four inclined planes on the Hayle Railway; those on the main line between Hayle and Redruth – at Angarrack and Penponds – were later bypassed by the West Cornwall Railway. Angarrack and Portreath inclines were worked by stationary steam engines, using coal imported from south Wales. The modern A30 Trunk Road has been included as a guide.

Initially locomotives were hauled up the Tresavean incline by rope; its gradient was 1 in 15. Ropes were prone to break and operations here and at Portreath were later undertaken using steel cables. By the early twentieth century the GWR had evolved a procedure for working the plane. Wagons, usually four in number and empty, would be shunted onto the down line at the foot of the plane. The locomotive would then run

The Portreath incline, on a branch of the Hayle Railway. It was worked from 1837 until 1932. *Pope/Parkhouse Archive*

Tresavean incline, formerly of the Hayle Railway, June 1933.
Maurice Dart Collection

Levant Mine, Zawn Brinny inclined plane, circa 1895.
Royal Institution of Cornwall

light engine to the head of the plane on the other track. It would then bring loaded wagons to the incline head where they were attached to the cable. This train would then descend the bank, hauling the up the empty wagons from the foot, on the other end of the cable. Four loaded wagons would take between seven and eight minutes to descend.[8]

Levant Mine, St Just in Penwith
SW 369346

The Zawn Brinny incline here was twin track and narrow gauge and ran up from a tunnel to the stamps, taking ore for processing. It was active in the period 1890-1930, when the mine closed. In the period 1820 to 1930 Levant produced over 130,000 tons of copper ore of high grade and 24,000 tons of black tin. In 1912 5,278 ounces of silver and 4 ounces of gold were also sold.[9] The site is now owned by the National Trust and accessible.

Lizard RNLI Lifeboat Station, Kilcobben Cove, Landewednack
SW 71521255

At Kilcobben Cove, on the Lizard, the RNLI installed a lift system in 1961 to take boatmen from the cliff top to their lifeboat at the cove and to provide a facility for raising casualties and for delivering equipment and supplies. A replacement inclined plane was installed in 1995. The electrically-powered single-track railway was built to a gauge of 8 feet and is 148 feet long. The passenger car covers the distance in less than one and a half minutes. More recently a new station has been built to take the latest all-weather Tamar class lifeboat and the cliff lift has been modified with the installation of an upgraded drum drive unit. The complex was largely complete by the end of 2011. Viewable from the cliff top.

National Explosives Company, Gwithian
SW 57803975 FOOT OF INCLINE

Following the invention of dynamite by Alfred Nobel in 1866, the National Explosives Company was established by Shilson at Hayle Towans, in Gwithian parish in 1888. The location was ideal: high dunes would screen any accidental explosion from other process buildings – deliberately sited apart – and so limit its effects.

Around 1905 a new plant consisting of nitrating house, separating house and two storage houses was built in the high dunes near the engine shaft of the old Boiling Well mine. A 2-foot gauge railway linked the separate processes and a winch-operated cable-worked inclined plane hauled up tanks of mixed acid and glycerine, carried on a specially designed wagon or rail-mounted cradle, to the nitrating house by the summit. It was about 350 feet long, rising into the dunes. By 1904 the factory at Hayle Towans was already an extensive complex and during World War I at least 1,800 staff were employed here. The entire site was closed after the war ended, in 1919.[10]

Sennen Cove, St Just in Penwith
SW 355263

A private, single-track, electrically-powered funicular with a gauge of 690mm serves a residence.

St Keverne Quarries: Quarry Tramway, St Keverne
SW 807226 FOOT – SW 808224 HEAD

A series of coastal quarries existed at Porthallow and Porthoustock, on the Lizard. Here quarrying for gabbro – a rock similar to basalt – had been undertaken since the late nineteenth century and in 1912 a narrow gauge railway was built. It ran about a mile from the quarries at Porthallow towards Porthoustock, the final section consisting of a double-track inclined plane from the beach at Porthkerris Cove to a crusher plant. Beneath the plant a second railway took the crushed stone a further half mile to a jetty with a concrete silo at Batty's Point, Porthoustock. Here horses hauled wagons until replaced by locomotives in 1934. A second, separate, inclined plane served a further quarry near the route – at

Incline from Porthkerris Cove, St Keverne Quarries tramway, 1998. *Maurice Dart*

SW 808222. The quarries, last worked by a subsidiary of Amalgamated Roadstone Corporation, closed in 1958. The incline is walkable.[11]

St Michaels Mount Cliff Railway, Marazion
SW 51473000 FOOT – SW51462986 HEAD

One little known line is the freight-only single track cable incline that runs in tunnel from the harbour at St Michael's Mount to the castle on the cliffs above. It is not open to the public. A single wagon is the sole rolling stock. The railway was constructed in 1912 and apart from some peat railways in Northern Ireland it was the only line in the UK built to the 2 foot 5½ inch or 750mm gauge; it has since been re-gauged to 2 foot 5 inches. The railway rises 173 feet and is about 650 feet long. The gradient is gentle near the quay, but approaching the summit, in the rock tunnel, it steepens to about 1 in 2. Power was provided by a single-cylinder Ruston petrol engine; that was replaced by a battery operated 20 horsepower DC motor which in turn was superseded by a 12 horsepower Crompton Parkinson AC unit in the 1950s.[12]

Wheal Friendly, St Agnes

SW 72085141

At St Agnes, Wheal Friendly was a tin mine, part of the West Wheal Kitty group, located in Trevaunance Combe. Here a double-track tramway incline took ore to the road in Trevaunance Combe for processing at Jericho Stamps in Trevellas Combe. The mine was active in the late nineteenth century: the incline was a late development, installed in the early twentieth century. Closure came in 1913.[13]

Wheal Friendly, Trevaunance Combe, St Agnes. Steep double-track inclined plane running onto trestles by the road at the foot of the combe. *Clive Benney Collection*

Wheal Owles, St Just in Penwith

SW 36503225 FOOT, KENIDJACK
SW 36843218 HEAD, WHEAL BOYS

Wheal Owles was a successful tin mine, which was worked from 1815 to 1893. The sett incorporated mines at Wheal Boys and Wheal Drea. At some stage during the nineteenth century – possibly in the 1850s – surface works were developed to include an extensive system, known as the Parknoweth Tramway, which incorporated possibly two inclines. The main incline ran from Wheal Boys to the valley floor at Kenidjack, near Wheal Drea. In 1873 the tramway here was described as *'partly level and partly on an incline so steep that an engine assists in drawing waggons up and in checking their descent'*. In September that year Captain John Boyns was injured by three wagons which ran away before being attached to the cable at the head of the plane. In 1875 an eleven-year-old boy was killed, attempting to joy ride on moving wagons on the incline.[14] The mines here closed following a flood disaster at West Wheal Owles in January 1893.

The Kenidjack valley is now very overgrown, even in winter, and the formation of the incline is largely hidden.

Wheal Trewavas, Breage, near Porthleven

SW 599265

Wheal Trewavas was established in 1834. An inclined plane was cut through rock from the cliff top. An engine house was built on a ledge part way down the cliff edge; the incline was used, no doubt, in its erection and the delivery of its steam engine. These operations would have demanded great engineering skill. By 1836 mining was being undertaken and ores were hauled from the shaft up the plane by a horse whim at the incline head. The mine closed in 1846 when the workings flooded.[15] In the brief period the mine worked, the ore recovered was worth £78,981. In 2008 the site was acquired by the National Trust.

Glossary

Adit
Roughly horizontal access or drainage tunnel in a mine.

Andesite
Volcanic rock containing feldspar; the fine-grained equivalent of diorite.

Banksman
Incline operative usually stationed at the foot of an inclined plane. Known as a pitman in a claypit or quarry.

Blondin
A form of aerial ropeway named after Charles Blondin, the French tightrope walker.

Brakesman
Incline operative usually stationed at the head of an inclined plane; often the plane manager, in charge of its operation.

Bucket-in-a-well.
A system of haulage on inclined planes using the weight of water as motive power. Promoted by Robert Fulton and used at Hobbacott and later, unsuccesfully, at Wellisford.

Bucketway
See cableway.

Cableway
A suspended cable used for carrying ore, rock or spoil in buckets.

Caisson
In this context a boat lift consisting of a watertight wooden or iron box able to contain a narrow boat – and its crew – raised or lowered by means of racks and pinions, within a deep water-filled lock chamber. Closely-fitting doors at the ends of the caisson and lock allowed boats to enter or leave at the head or foot of the chamber.

Counter-balance
In this context relating to a gravity-operated inclined plane. A funicular is a good example. A water counter-balanced incline uses the weight of water carried by a wagon or car at the head of an incline to raise a second attached to the same cable up the incline.

Culm
Small coal; anthracite, better than 'slack'.

Decauville track
Narrow-gauge track introduced in the 1870s for agricultural purposes by Paul Decauville. The name became generic in France for portable track. Used to supply the trenches in World War I.

Dimension stone
Hard-wearing stone that has been cut to specific sizes or shapes. Granite, limestone, marble and slate are examples of stones that can be used as dimension stone.

Dog hole
Foot of an incline – known as a skip road – from a china clay pit to sky tip.

Dolerite
Fine-grained igneous rock.

Elvan
Term used in the south west for greenstone, a variety of quartz-porphyry.

Feldbahn
German term for a narrow-gauge industrial or military railway.

Feldspar
Hard rock-forming minerals in igneous rocks.

Flat rods
Iron, wood or wire reciprocating rods transferring power from a waterwheel or steam engine to a remote shaft.

Funicular
Cable railway with counter-balanced ascending and descending cars. The term is commonly used for passenger or cliff railways.

Gabbro
Coarse-grained igneous rock containing feldspar, similar but coarser than basalt.

Gin
See horse whim.

Grizzley
Coarse screening plant eliminating oversized rock or ore from entering a transfer system.

Haematite, micaceous
Haematite, or hematite, is the mineral form of iron. Micaceous is a term used to indicate its specific structure: it contains mica.

Horse whim or horse gin
Machine for hoisting ore or clay from a pit or mine, sometimes utilising an inclined plane, powered by a horse or horses walking a circuit round a wooden drum, around which a cable was wound or unwound.

Jaw crusher
Compression crusher utilising two metal plates.

Knocker line
A signalling system using a steel wire adjacent to the incline (or within a mine shaft) to transmit mechanical signals by bell or other means to the hoist operator.

Launder
An elevated leat or aqueduct.

Leat
Man-made water channel bringing water from a weir on a river or stream to a mill or water-pump, or – in other contexts – used for irrigation.

Main-and-tail
A double-drum reversible haulage system used on a single track inclined plane with variable gradient. The 'main' rope hauls a set of wagons or tubs up the plane; the 'tail' rope is attached to the rear of the set. With the tubs emptied, the tail rope is wound in, the main rope left to run free and the set is returned to the foot of the plane.

Marl
Clay soil.

Plateway
Early tramway using flanged cast-iron rails, or 'L' plates.

Rack-and-pinion
In this context, a rack railway or an inclined plane utilising a pair of gears. A rotating pinion on a railcar engages a linear rack on the incline, thus controlling the car's ascent or descent. But see also entry for 'caisson'.

Self-acting incline
Gravity-worked incline; descending loaded wagons haul up empties.

Sett
Granite block (or other stone) used as a base for a wooden or iron tramway. Forerunner of the 'sleeper'. But the term is also used for the ground licenced to a group of miners within which minerals could be extracted.

Slack
Small coal, coal dust, fragments.

Slimes
Mine waste, reworked at mineries such as those on the Mendip Hills.

Stamps
Stamping mill used to crush ores by pounding by timber or iron lifters, with iron heads, commonly powered by a waterwheel.

Stope
A stepped excavation employed when mining ores from steeply inclined veins of ore.

Tramway
Generic term for mineral railways, often narrow-gauge, sometimes horse-drawn, but later used by steam locomotives; to some extent interchangeable with tramroad.

Tramroad
Also known as a wagonway. A road prepared for wagons, utilising beams of cut timber, blocks of stone or plates of iron; a forerunner of a modern railway.

Tramplate
A flanged cast iron plate or 'L' plate, used in a plateway or early tramway.

Track, interlaced
Two sets of rails overlap on the same formation, on a tramway, but do not connect. A layout adopted where width is restricted, for example on a bridge or in a tunnel.

Wolfram
Another name for tungsten.

References

Inclined plane designers

1 Hadfield, 1966, 151-152; Shrophire RO 972, parcel 245, map of 1794; Russell, 1971, 144

2 Trinder, 2000, 67

3 M. W. Doughty, 'Samborne Palmer's Diary: Technological innovation by a Somerset coal-mine owner'. *Industrial Archaeology Review*, III, 1978, 17-28

4 Fulton, 1796

5 Keast, 1982

6 Michael R. Lane, 'Marks, George Croydon, Baron Marks (1858–1938)', rev., *Oxford Dictionary of National Biography*, Oxford University Press, 2004

Gazetteer

Section 1, pages 16-21

The Bristol Avon

1 Day 1987, 36; *Bath Chronicle* 23 June 1808

2 Egan, 1819

3 Day 1987, 23; personal communication, Ken Kemp, 27 July 2011

4 Maggie Shapland, 'Clifton Rocks Railway Refurbishment', *BIAS Journal* 38, 9-21; Oppitz,1990

5 Brindle, 2005, 76-77

6 Mike Chapman, 'A Visit to the Inclined Planes along the K&A Canal between Dundas and Avoncliff'. *Weigh-House* 48, October 2007, 6-9; Sir Arthur Elton, 'The Pre-History of Railways', *Somerset Archaeological and Natural History Society Proceedings*, 107, 1963, 54

7 Hateley, 1977, H109; Ordnance Survey map, Gloucestershire 1904, 1:2,500

8 Bristol City Council Historic Environment Record No. 1891M, recorded by D. Pollard in 1984

9 Mike Chapman, 'A Visit to the Inclined Planes along the K&A Canal between Dundas and Avoncliff'. *Weigh-House* 48, October 2007, 6-9

10 *Bristol Times and Mirror*, article, 1883; personal communication Alan Tucker 24 July 2011

11 C. G. Down, 'Paradise Bottom', *The Industrial Railway Record*, 22, December 1968, 354-356

12 Mike Chapman, 'A Walk along the Route of Ralph Allen's Tramway between Combe Down and Bath', *Weigh-House* 53, April 2009, 14-15

13 Lewis 1970, 126

Section 2, pages 22-30

North and North-east Somerset

Main sources:

- Down, C. G. and Warrington, A. J., 2005

- Gould, S, 1999

1 Clew, 1986, 25-64

2 Hateley, 1977, H90; Mike Chapman, 'The Canal and Fullers Earth Works at Combe Hay', *Weigh-House*, 45, May 2006, 8

3 www.portisheadweb.org.uk/wcpr/conygar.html

4 Mike Chapman, 'A Visit to Colliery Sites related to the Coal Canal in Farmborough, High Littleton and Clutton'. *Weigh-House* 52, January 2009, 15

5 Mike Chapman, 'A Note on Hodshill Fullers Earth Mine', *Weigh-House* 54, September 2009, 12-15

6. C. G. Down, 'Kilmersdon Colliery Incline', *The Industrial Railway Record*, 18, April 1968, 204-209

7. Cornwell, 2005, 36-37

8. Mike Chapman, 'A Walk from the Canal at Durcott to Lower Conygre Colliery', *Weigh-House* 27, Summer 1999, 5-7

9. Mike Chapman, 'A Visit to the Site of Kilmersdon Colliery and Inclined Plane', *Weigh-House* 55, January 2010, 13

10. C. G. Down, 'Narrow Gauge Wagons: Lime Kiln Wagons', *The Industrial Railway Record* 60, 48-49

11. Atthill, 1984, 162

12. Somerset Historic Environment Record 23843; Ordnance Survey 1:2,500 map of 1886

13. Mike Chapman, 'A Walk along the Line of the Welton Tramway', *Weigh-House* 47, June 2007, 20

Section 3, pages 31-37

Somerset - the Mendips to the Blackdowns

1. Buchanan and Buchanan, 1980, 115; Warren, 1996, 18

2. George, 1997, 134

3. David Greenfield, 'The Tone Aqueduct at Creech St Michael', *Somerset Industrial Archaeological Society Bulletin* 90, August 2002, 2-3, citing Whitelaw, J, *Description of Whitelaw & Stirrat's Patent Water-Mill*, London 1843, 11, and *Minutes of the Proceedings of the Institution of Civil Engineers*, vol 13, 1853-4, 210, 213; Nick Kelly, 'The Water-powered Canal Incline in the British Isles'. *Proceedings of the Thirteenth Mill Research Conference*, ed Duncan Breckels, 1996, 40

4. Chard History Group, undated, 31

5. Brian Murless, personal communication, August 2011; W. I. Stanton and A. G. Clarke, 'Cornish Miners at Charterhouse-on-Mendip', in *Proc.UBSS*, Vol 17, 1,1984, 29-54

6. Warren, 1996, 23

7. Fairclough and Shepherd, 1975; Hateley, 1977, H70

8. Brian Murless, personal communication, 25 August 2011; Hateley, 1977, H58

9. Harris, 1996, 104-111; George, 1997, 127-131

10. Hateley, 1977, H75; Ordnance Survey map 1:2,500 for 1903

11. Legg, 1991, 31-32, 81-82; www.willys-mb.co.uk.htm; National Maritime Museum website

12. Nick Kelly, 'The Water-powered Canal Incline in the British Isles'. *Proceedings of the Thirteenth Mill Research Conference*, ed Duncan Breckels, 1996, 37

13. Brian Murless, personal communication, July 2011; Ordnance Survey 25-inch maps, 1886, 1903; Coysh, Mason and Waite, 1954, 51

Section 4, pages 38-43

Dorset and East Devon

1. Stanier and Cox, 2007; Stanier, 2002, 125; Ordnance Survey maps, Dorset 1:10,560, for 1903 and 1938, and 1:2,500 for 1903; Jackson, 1999, 67, 121

2. *Dorset County Chronicle & Somersetshire Gazette* 21 July 1881, page 7

3. Kidner, 2000, 87; personal communication, Geoff Roughton, April 2011; Ordnance Survey 1:2,500 maps for 1889, 1901 and 1928

4. Wood and Carter, 1999, 31; personal communications – Derrick Warren, March 2009 and January 2010

5. The Heritage Trail website

6. Hateley, 1977, H129; 1:2,500 Ordnance Survey maps, Parkston area, 1902, 1924, 1933 and 1953

7. Jackson, 1999, 19-58; Stanier and Cox, 2007; Stanier, 1995, 73; Stanier, 2002, 117-118

8. M. J. Messenger, 'The Portesham Tramway', *The Industrial Railway Record*, 9, March 1966, 280-281; Hateley, 1977, H134

Section 5, pages 44-55

Exmoor, North Devon and Lundy

1. http://www.bampton.org.uk/quarries.html

2. M. J. Messenger, 'Berry's Quarry', *The Industrial Railway Record*, 7, 1977, 129; Neil Parkhouse. 'Combe Martin - An Industrial Slum!?', *Archive* 7, September 1995, 7

3. Personal communication, Barry Hughes, 19 August 2011; Peter Christie, 1989, 43

4 Atkinson, M., ed, 1997, 34

5 Jones, M. H., 2011, 60-90, 238, 265-6

6 Hughes, 2006, 64-65; personal communication, 3 August 2011

7 Jones, M. H., 2011, 18, 131, 137-8

8 Jones, M. H., 2011, 318-320, 376-7; Hateley, 1977, H70

9 Personal communications – Brian Murless and Geoff Roughton; English Heritage: Pastscape website. NMR 1365645

10 Personal communication Brian Murless 2010

11 Dart, 2007; Rothwell and Ternstrom, 2008, 32-83

12 Dart, 2007; Robert Humm, '4ft 8½in and all that. The British gauge survey'. *The Railway Magazine*, September 2008, 23; Oppitz, 1990, 134-137

13 B. D. Hughes, personal communication, 19 August 2011, citing *North Devon Journal*, 1856, [issue not known]

14 Atkinson, M., ed, 1997, 109

15 Messenger, 2006, 95; Dart, 2007; Dart, 2010, 120

16 Williams, 1978

17 Peter Daniel, 'A Limekiln at Nurcott, Luxborough'. *Somerset Industrial Archaeological Society Bulletin* 118, December 2011, 6-17; Ordnance Survey map, 1888, 1:2,500

18 Warren, ed, 1996, 52; Jeboult, 1893; Chris Tilley, personal communication 4 October 2011

19 Hughes, 2006, 44-45, 76

20 Hughes, 2006, 55, 64; personal communication 3 August 2011

21 B. D. Hughes, personal communication, 19 August 2011; A. H. Slee, 'Some Dead Industries of North Devon', *Transactions of the Devonshire Association*, 1938, 218-9

Section 6, pages 56-63

Dartmoor

1 Personal communication Barry Hughes 19 August 2011; Plymouth & West Devon Record Office, 1415/25/1; Anne Born, 'Limestone, Limekilns and the Limeburning Industry North and West of Dartmoor', *Trans. Devonshire Association*, 123, 1991, 238

2 Dines, 1956, 732; Hamilton Jenkin, 2005, 126-7. Devon Record Office: mine plans, R 54B Bagtor; Doug Westaway, personal communication, 5 August 2011

3 Michael Messenger, personal communication, 2011

4 aditnow.co.uk

5 Hamilton-Jenkin, 2005, 111; Doug Westaway, Torquay, personal communication, February 2011; Mine plan R79F at Devon Record Office

6 Richardson, 1995, 37-39, 43

7 Brooks, 2004, 45, 58-59, 75, 79, 106, 130

8 Hamilton Jenkin, 2005; Hateley, 1977, H48

9 Richardson, 1995, 27-35; Atkinson, M., et al, 1978, 32-34; Phil Newman, personal comunication, 9 September 2011

10 Phil Newman, 2006, 4-6; Owen Baker, *DTRG Newsletter* 33, July 2007, 6; Ordnance Survey map 1890, 1:10,560.

11 Doug Westaway, personal communication, 1 February 2011

12 Anne Born, 'Limestone, Limekilns and the Limeburning Industry North and West of Dartmoor', *Trans. Devonshire Association*, 123, 1991, 238; OS maps 1884 and 1906 1:2,500

13 *Woolmer's Gazette* 9 February 1839 p 1 col 4;

14 Devon Record office 62/9/2/Box 2/40 of 31-9-1880, Anne Born, 'Limestone, Limekilns and the Limeburning Industry North and West of Dartmoor', *Trans. Devonshire Association*, 123, 1991, 238; OS 1: 2,500 of 1884

15 Dart, 2007; Anne Born, 'Limestone, Limekilns and the Limeburning Industry North and West of Dartmoor', *Trans. Devonshire Association*, 123, 1991, 224

16 Atkinson et al, 1978, 32-34; Richardson, 1992, 27-35; Brooks, 2004, 159-161

17 Doug Westaway, personal communication, 1 February 2011

18 Richardson, 1995, 37-39, 43

19 Phil Newman, personal communications, 30 August, 9 September 2011

20 Hateley, 1977, H42

21 Anne Born, 'Limestone, Limekilns and the Limeburning

Industry North and West of Dartmoor', *Trans. Devonshire Association*, 123, 1991, 221, 225, 238-239; Devon Record office 62/9/2/Box 2/40 of 31-9-1880

22 Michael Messenger, personal communication, 2011; Anne Born, 'Limestone, Limekilns and the Limeburning Industry North and West of Dartmoor', *Trans. Devonshire Association*, 123, 1991, 223, 235

23 Hamilton Jenkin, 2005, 123; Michael Messenger, personal communication, 2008;

24 Doug Westaway, email February 2011

25 Stanier, 1999, 7, 20-21, citing: *Journal of the Rev Bray*, quoted in Bray, Mrs E. A., *A Description of the part of Devonshire bordering on the Tamar and the Tavy .. in a series of letters to Robert Southey, Esq.* Vol 1, 1836, 286

26 Messenger, 2005, 39; OS maps 1:10,560 of 1888-90 and 1907; Anne Born, 'Limestone, Limekilns and the Limeburning Industry North and West of Dartmoor', *Trans. Devonshire Association*, 123, 1991, 238

27 Ian P. Peaty, 'Wilminstone Quarry', *Railway Bylines*, March 2009, 192-197

Section 7, pages 64-69
South Devon and South-west Dartmoor
1 Friends of Babbacombe Cliff Railway web site

2 Funicular Railways of the UK. Mark Hows web site

3 Dart, 2007, plate 65

4 Stephen Lynas, 'Bulkamore Iron Mine', in *The Book of Rattery*, Halsgrove, 2001, 94; Richardson, 1995, 87

5 Bone and Stanier, 1998, 50

6 Hall, 1963, 12-14

7 Wade, 2004, 43, 53

8 David Muir. *Plym Bridge Woods*. The National Trust, undated leaflet

9 Hateley, 1977, H49; Kingdom, 1998, 23

10 Ordnance Survey 1:2,500 map of Devon, 1955

Section 8, pages 70-79
The Lower Tamar Valley and South-east Cornwall
1 Barton, 1964, 65; Booker, 1971, 180-191, citing C. R. Clinker, *Railway Magazine*, May 1951

2 Richardson, 1995, 95, 99-100; 2 Colin Buck, 'Preliminary Assessment of Industrial Sites of Archaeological Importance in the Tamar Valley - Part II', *Tamar Journal*, 24, 2002, 27

3 Rick Stewart, personal communications, 29 August and 5 September 2011

4 J. H. Murchison, 'The Devonshire Great Consolidated Copper Mines - 1850'. *Mining Journal* 26 October 1850, 506-507

5 Barton, 1964, 75-76; Booker, 1971, 157; Hamilton Jenkin, 2005, 15; *Tavistock Gazette*, December issues 1864; Colin Buck, 'Devon Great Consols Mine', *Tamar Journal* 25, 2003, 19

6 Andrew Pye and Peter Weddell. 'A Survey of the Gawton Mine & Arsenic Works', *Tamar Journal* 14, 1992, 25

7 Booker, 1971, 266; Barton, 1964, 69

8 Personal communication, Michael Messenger; Cornwall Record Office – CF/1/3744 of 1840; CF/1/3745 of October 1885 and PP/567 of 1907

9 Buck, 1988; Hateley, 1977, H22; Barton, 1964, 69

10 Fairclough and Shepherd, 1975, 33; www.trainweb.org/railwest/railco; Peter Herring, c2000, 44

11 Anthony Power, 'Morwellham Quay 2005', *Tamar Journal* 28, 2006, 59; Robert Waterhouse, personal communication 6 September 2011; Colin Buck, 'New Quay, An Archaeological Investigation', *Tamar Journal* 33, 2011, 32

12 C. Gaskell Brown and R. Coleman-Smith, 'The Archaeology of Newquay', *Trans. Devonshire Association* 114, December 1982, 133-167; Robert Waterhouse, personal communication 6 September 2011; Colin Buck, 'New Quay, An Archaeological Investigation', *Tamar Journal* 33, 2011, 32-33

13 Hateley, 1977, H18; Pye and Woodward, 1996, 88-89, 1896 map of Scraesdon – The National Archives: WO 78/2314

14 Booker, 1971, 31, 114-115

15 Robert Waterhouse, personal communication 6 September 2011; Isham 2000, 68-71

16 Michael Messenger, 'Early Cornish Mineral Railways', *Trevithick Society Journal,* 5, 1977, 72-73

17 Booker, 1971, 131

18 Uhlemann, 2002; Egerton, 1812

19 Brooke, 2001, 12

Section 9, pages 80-87

North and East Cornwall

1 Cornwall and Scilly Historic Environment Record - SMR 56815 - MCO36270; Ordnance Survey first edition 1:2,500

2 George, 1997, 50, 78; Harris and Ellis, 1972; Young and Dudley Stamp, 1998, 29

3 1851 Census, Bridgerule - HO107 1896 f 428 p 6

4 *Bude and Stratton Post* 16 October 1858

5 Hadfield, 1967

6 Hateley, 1977, H4; Stanier, 1999; Dart, 2004

7 Stanier, 1995, 114-115; Hateley, 1977, H12; Lorigan, 2007, 52-54; *Royal Cornwall Gazette* 27 August 1886; personal communication, Michael Messenger, 15 July 2011

8 Peter Joseph, 'Durfold China Clay Works, Bodmin: its history, interpretation and regeneration'. *Journal of the Trevithick Society*, 28, 2001, 61-62

9 Messenger, 2001, 86, 88; Stanier, 1999, 106

10 Michael Messenger, personal communication, May 2011

11 Sharpe, 1990

12 Messenger, 2005, 38

13 Godden and Fellgett, 2000, 5

14 Michael Messenger, 1978, 34

15 Brown and Acton, 1999, 132 & 139

Section 10, pages 88-99

Mid Cornwall

1 Keast, 1982

2 Smith, 1992, 12-13

3 Isham, 2000, 95-96, citing Cornwall Record Office, TF1056 of 1851; Michael Messenger, personal communication, 15 July 2011

4 *Royal Cornwall Gazette* 31 May 1844; Smith, 1988

5 Maurice Dart, personal communication, September 2011

6 Dart, 2010, 28

7 Lewis, J, 1997, 38, 52-3, 133, Ordnance Survey map, 25", sheet 51.6 of 1881; Atkinson, B, 1988, 56; Barton, 1964, 19; *Royal Cornwall Gazette* 28 January 1859 p 6

8 Brooks, 2011, 65-68, citing: Charles Perran, *North of England Mining Institute of Mining and Mechanical Engineers*, Vol 27, 1877-8.

9 Dr K. D. Russ and R. F. Morton, 'Digging Back in Time: An Adit Clearance Project at Polgooth, Cornwall'. *The Bulletin of the Peak District Mines Historical Society* Volume 13, 2, Winter 1996, 151-3; Acton, 1992, 13

10 Maurice Dart, personal communication, September 2011; Michael Messenger, personal communication December 2011

11 C. M. Bristow, 'Late 18th and early 19th century forays into economic geology – some little-known Franco-German papers describing Carclaze Old Pit, St Austell'. *Proceedings of the Ussher Society*, 2008

12 P. Sheppard, Cornwall Archaeological Society, *Cornish Archaeology*, 15, 1976, 110; Cornwall Record Office - TF/3200 - 17 March 1859

13 Vaughan, 2008, 85

14 Ordnance Survey map 1881, at 1:2500

15 Smith, 1992, 35; Stanier, 1995, 32; Ordnance Survey map 1971, at 1:2,500

16 Isham, 2000, 68-71; Pennycross census, Plymouth, 1851. HO 107 1877 f 709

17 Messenger, 2001, 19, 21, 25, citing CRO Bor/Lisk 393 and CRO PDR 10/2, 10/7; Isham, 2000, 71-72, citing *Royal Cornwall Gazette* 12 October 1855; *Moorswater -*

An archaeological survey, Cornwall Archaeological Unit, 1999, 26-7; kiln survey by Martin Watts 1978

18 Isham, 2000, 157

19 Hateley, 1977, H22

20 Keast, 1982, 122-143

21 Smith, 1988, 69

22 Cornwall in Focus web site

23 Brooks, 2011, 21-30, 37

24 *Royal Cornwall Gazette* 31 May 1844

25 *Royal Cornwall Gazette* 14 June 1839

26 Brooks, 2011, 36-51; Geoff Roughton, personal communication April 2011

27 Hadfield, 1967, 165-167

28 Hateley, 1977, H4; personal communication Michael Messenger

29 Smith, 1988, 66

30 Hateley, 1977, H23; Messenger, 2006, 48; Rex Wailes, 'Water-Driven Mills for Grinding Stone', *Trans. Newcomen Society*, 39, 1966-67, 106-107

31 Dart, 2005, plate XXIX

32 Jim Lewis, 'A Recent History of Wheal Prosper, Lanivet', *Trevithick Society Journal*, 35, 2008, 112, 114

Section 11, pages 100-106

West Cornwall

1 Hateley, 1977, H2

2 Brown and Acton, 1994, 104-116; *Royal Cornwall Gazette* 24 April 1863 p 8; Ordnance Survey maps, 1:2,500 for 1876-8 and 1908; *Cornish Telegraph* 5 January 1872; Stoyel and Williams, 2001, 12, 16-20

3 Brown and Acton, 1995, 127

4 Roger Langley, 'Richard Thomas of Falmouth', *Trevithick Society Journal*, 35, 2008, 30

5 *Royal Cornwall Gazette* 26 May 1843 and 5 June 1846

6 St John Thomas and Clinker, 1960, 102; Acton, 1997, 79-80, 159;

7 Census returns for Illogan – 1871: RG10 2322 f41 p18; 1881: RG11 2333 f97 p2; 1891: RG12 1849 f89 p 3; 1901: RG13 2242 f83 p8

8 Dart, 2005a; Jenkins and Langley, 2002, 12, 19, 21

9 Cornwall in Focus web site

10 Earl, 1978, 185, 236, 246

11 Hateley, 1977, H16; Dart, 2005, illus 84-86, plate XXVI; www.irsociety.co.uk/Archives/20/ARC.htm

12 Dart, 2005, illus 87-89; Messenger, 2006, 80

13 Brown and Acton, 1997, 84, 88

14 Hateley, 1977, H24; Dart, 2010, 91; *Cornish Telegraph* 24 September 1873 and 31 March 1875

15 Brown and Acton, 1995, 144-145

Bibliography

Acton, Bob, *Exploring Cornwall's Tramway Trails, Volume 1,* Landfall Publications, 1997

Atkinson, Barry, *Mining Sites in Cornwall and West Devon*, Dyllansow, Truran, 1988

Atkinson, Michael, ed., *Exmoor's Industrial Archaeology*, Exmoor Books, 1997

Atkinson, Michael, et al, *Dartmoor Mines. The Mines of the Granite Mass.* Exeter Industrial Archaeology Group, 1978

Atthill, Robin, *Old Mendip*, Bran's Head Books, 1984

Barton, D. B., *A Historical Survey of the Mines and Mineral Tramways of East Cornwall and West Devon*, Bradford Barton, 1964

Bone, Mike, and Stanier, Peter, *A Guide to the Industrial Archaeology of Devon, Association for Industrial Archaeology*, 1998

Booker, Frank, *Industrial Archaeology of the Tamar Valley*, David & Charles, 1971

Brindle, Steven, *Brunel: The Man Who Built the World*, Phoenix, 2006

Brooke, Justin, trans and ed., *The Kalmeter Journal*, Twelveheads Press, 2001

Brooks, Tony, *Great Rock, Devon's Last 'Metal' Mine*, Cornish Hillside Publications, 2004

Brooks, Tony, *A History of Iron Mining In Cornwall*, Cornish Hillside Publications, 2011

Brown, Kenneth, and Acton, Bob, *Exploring Cornish Mines, Volume 1*, Landfall Publications, 1994

Brown, Kenneth, and Acton, Bob, *Exploring Cornish Mines, Volume 2*, Landfall Publications, 1995

Brown, Kenneth, and Acton, Bob, *Exploring Cornish Mines, Volume 3*, Landfall Publications, 1997

Brown, Kenneth, and Acton, Bob, *Exploring Cornish Mines, Volume 4*. Landfall Publications, 1999

Buchanan, C. A., Buchanan, R. A., *Industrial Archaeology of Central Southern England*, 1980

Buck, Colin, *Gunnislake Clitters Mine*, Cornwall County Council, 1988

Clew, Kenneth R., *The Somersetshire Coal Canal & Railways*, Brans Head Books, 1986

Cornwell, John, *Collieries of Somerset & Bristol*, Landmark Publishing, 2005

Coysh, A. W., Mason, E. J. and Waite, V., *The Mendips*, Robert Hale, 1954

Dart, Maurice, *Cornwall Narrow Gauge*, Middleton Press, 2005

Dart, Maurice, *West Cornwall Mineral Railways*, Middleton Press, 2005a

Dart, Maurice, *Devon Narrow Gauge*, Middleton Press, 2007

Dart, Maurice, *Images of Industrial and Narrow Gauge Railways - Devon*, Halsgrove 2010

Dart, Maurice, *Images of Industrial & Narrow Gauge Railways – Cornwall*, Halsgrove, 2010

Day, Joan, *A Guide to the Industrial Heritage of Avon*. Association for Industrial Archaeology, 1987

Dines, H. G., *The Metalliferous Mining Region of South West England, Volume II*, Her Majesty's Stationery Office, 1956

Down, C. G. and Warrington, A. J., *The History of the Somerset Coalfield*, Radstock Museum, 2005

Egan, Pierce, *Walks through Bath*, Bath 1819

Egerton, Francis, *Description du Plan Incliné Souterrain*, Paris, 1812

Fairclough, Tony and Shepherd, Eric, *Mineral Railways of the West Country*, Bradford Barton, 1975

Fulton, Robert, *Report on the Proposed Canal between the Rivers Heyl and Helford*, London 1796.

George, Brian, *James Green, Canal Builder and County Surveyor*, Devon Books, 1997

Gibson, Bryan, *The Lee Moor Tramway*, Plymouth Railway Circle, 1993

Godden, James and Fellgett, Mary, *The Parish of St Kew, North Cornwall, Volume Two*, privately published 2000

Hadfield, Charles, *The Canals of South West England*, David & Charles, 1967

Hall, R. M. S., *The Lee Moor Tramway*, Oakwood Press, 1963

Hamilton-Jenkin, A. K., *Mines of Devon*, Landmark Publications, 2005

Harris, Helen, and Ellis, Monica, *The Bude Canal,* David & Charles, 1972

Harris, Helen, *The Grand Western Canal*, Devon Books, 1996

Herring, Peter, *The Archaeology of Kit Hill*, Cornwall Archaeology Unit, undated, circa 2000

Hughes, Barry D., *Rolle Canal & The North Devon Limestone Trade*, Edward Gaskell, 2006

Hateley, Roger, *Industrial Locomotives of South Western England*, Industrial Railway Society, 1977

Isham, Ken, *Limekilns and Limeburners in Cornwall*, Cornish Hillside Publications, 2000

Jackson, B. L., *Isle of Portland Railways, Volume One, The Admiralty and Quarry Railway*, Oakwood Press 1999

Jeboult, Edward, *History of West Somerset*, 1893

Jenkins, S. C., and Langley, R.C., *The West Cornwall Railway*, The Oakwood Press, 2002

Jones, M. H., *The Brendon Hills Iron Mines and the West Somerset Mineral Railway. A New Account*, Lightmoor Press, 2011

Keast, John, *'The King of Mid-Cornwall'. The Life of Joseph Thomas Treffry (1782 - 1850)*, Dyllansow Truran, 1982

Kidner, R. W., R*ailways of Purbeck*, Oakwood Press, 2000

Kingdom, Anthony R., *The Plymouth to Yealmpton Railway*, Ark Publications 1998

Legg, Rodney, *Steep Holm at War*. Wincanton Press, 1991

Lewis, Jim, *A Richly Yielding Piece of Ground*, Cornish Hillside Publications, 1997

Lewis, M. J. T., *Early Wooden Railways*, Routledge & Kegan Paul, 1970

Lorigan, Catherine, *Delabole*, Pengelly Press, 2007

Messenger, Michael, *Caradon and Looe, The Canal, Railways and Mines*, Twelveheads Press, 2001

Messenger, Michael, *Industrial Railways of the South West*, Twelveheads Press, 2006

Mitchell, Vic, and Smith, Keith, *Dorset & Somerset Narrow Gauge*, Middleton Press, 2006

Muir, David, *Plym Bridge Woods*. The National Trust, undated leaflet

Newman, Phil, *Holne Chase Tin Mine, Holne, Devon*. English Heritage 2006

Oppitz, Leslie, *Tramways Remembered. West and South West England,* Countryside Books, 1990

Pye, Andrew, and Woodward, Freddie, *The Historic Defences of Plymouth*.
          Exeter Archaeology/Fortress Study Group South West, 1996

Richardson, P. H. G., *Mines of Dartmoor and the Tamar Valley*, 1995

Riley, Hazel, and Wilson-North, Robert, *The Field Archaeology of Exmoor*, English Heritage, 2001

Rolt, L. T. C., *George and Robert Stephenson*, Penguin Books, 1978

Russell, R., *Lost Canals of England and Wales*, 1971

Sharpe, Adam, *Coastal Slate Quarries, Tintagel to Trebarwith: archaeological survey for the National Trust*,
          Cornwall Archaeological Unit 1990.

Smith, John R., *The Luxulyan Valley*, Cornwall Archaeological Unit, Cornwall County Council, 1988

Smith, John R., *Cornwall's China Clay Heritage,* Cornwall Archaeological Unit, Twelveheads Press, 1992

Stanier, Peter, *Quarries of England and Wales, An Historic Photographic Record*, Twelveheads Press, 1995

Stanier, Peter, *South West Granite,* Cornish Hillside Publications, 1999

Stanier, Peter, *Dorset in the Age of Steam*, Dorset Books, 2002

Stanier, Peter and Cox, Peter, *Isle of Portland Industrial Archaeology Survey: Phase I Assessment Report*, AC Archaeology, March 2007

Stoyel, Alan and Williams, Peter, *Images of Cornish Tin*, Landmark Publishing/English Heritage, 2001

Thomas, David St J., and Clinker, C. R., *A Regional History of the Railways of Great Britain. Volume 1, The West Country*,
          Phoenix House, 1960

Thornes, Robin, *Men of Iron. The Fussells of Mells*. Frome Society for Local Study, 2010

Trinder, Barrie, *The Industrial Revolution in Shropshire*, Phillimore, 2000

Uhlemann, Hans-Joachim, *Canal Lifts and Inclines of the World*, 2002

Vaughan, John, *Rails to Newquay*, Oakwood Press, 2008

Wade, E. A., *The Redlake Tramway & China Clay Works*, Twelveheads Press, 2004

Warren, Derrick, ed. *Somerset's Industrial Heritage. A Guide and Gazetteer*. Somerset Industrial Archaeology Society, 1996

Williams, Edward F., *Parish Surveys in Somerset – 2 Luxborough*, Somerset Archaeological & Natural History Society, 1978

Wood, P. J., and Carter, R. W., *A History of the Parish of Chardstock*, privately published, 1999

Young, Bill and Dudley Stamp, Bryan, *Bude Canal, Past & Present*, privately published 1998

Index

A

Abbots Leigh
    Paradise Bottom Tramway 20
Abbotsbury branch railway 43
Abersychan 47
Admiralty Breakwater incline,
    Portland 39
Aggregate Industries plc 55
Albert, Wilhelm 9
Alder Quarry, Thrushelton 57
Allen, Ralph 16
Amalgamated Roadstone Corporation
    105
Angarrack Incline, Hayle 102
Antony
    Screasdon Incline 78
Ashwick
    New Moorewood Colliery incline 28
Axbridge Hill Iron Ochre Mine 32

B

Babbacombe Cliff Lift, Torquay 65
Bagtor Mine, Ilsington 57
Bailey's Quarry, Bampton 45
Basset Mines, Carn Brea, Redruth 101
Bath
    Ralph Allen's Tramway 21
Bathampton Down Quarry incline 17
Bearland Wood Mine 48
Belstone Quarry, Belstone 57
Berry's Quarry, Combe Martin 45
Bideford Black Culm Mine, Bideford 45
Blackfriars Bridge 76
Blackland Mine, Withypool 47

Blisland
    Durfold China Clay Works 85
Board, John 34
Bodmin Moor 85, 87
Boots, Torquay 65
Boscastle Slate Quarry, Trevalga 81
Boscawen Diagonal Shaft 101
Botallack Mine, St Just in Penwith 101
Bournemouth
    Bournemouth Corporation 41
    East Cliff and West Cliff Railways 41
    Fisherman's Walk railway 41
Bovey Tracey
    Kelly Mine 59
Boyns, Captain John 106
Braund, Ernest 48
Bray, Reverend 63
Braysdown Colliery incline 23
Breage
    Wheal Trewavas 106
Brendon Incline,West Somerset Mineral
    Railway, 47
Bridestowe
    Lower Stone Quarry 60
    Sourton Quarry 62
Bridford
    Bridford Quarry 57
    Paddy Dixon's Quarry 57
    Scatter Rocks Quarries 61
Bridgerule
    Merrifield Incline 81, 82
Bridgewater, Duke of 79
Bridgwater and Taunton Canal 13, 32

Brislington
    Ironmould Lane incline 19
Brislington House 19
Bristol
    Clifton Rocks Railway 17
    Netham Chemical Works incline 20
Bristol & Exeter Railway 34
Bristol and North Somerset Railway 25
Bristol Strontia Company 20
Brixton
    Steer Point Brickworks 69
Brown & May steam engine 34
Brown, Thomas 47
Brownstone Battery, Froward Point,
    Kingswear 65
Brunel, Isambard Kingdom 18
Bucks Mills limekilns 48
Bude Canal 13, 81, 82
Bugle
    Lantern China Clay Pit 93
Bulkamore Mine, Rattery 66
Buller, Sir Francis 12
Butler, Samuel 24

C

Cableways
    Blondin 10
    bucketway 10
Caffa Mill Pill incline, Fowey 13, 89
Caldy 48
California Colliery incline 17
Calstock
    Calstock inclined plane 71
    Greenhill Arsenic Works 75
    Gunnislake Clitters Mine 75

Camborne
    Grenville United Mines 102
    Penponds Incline 102
Camerton New Pit incline 23
Canal plane to Morwellham Quay 79
Canals
    Bridgwater and Taunton Canal 13, 32
    Bude Canal 12, 13, 81
    Chard Canal 13
    Dorset & Somerset Canal 29
    Feeder Canal, Bristol 20
    Grand Western Canal 13, 34
    Helston Canal 12
    Kennet and Avon Canal 16, 18, 19
    Par Canal 89
    Rolle Canal 13, 53
    Shropshire Canal 11
    Somersetshire Coal Canal 22, 26
    Somersetshire Coal Canal
      Committee 11
    St Columb Canal 88, 97
    Tavistock Canal 12, 77
    Torrington Canal 53
    tub boat canals 11, 12
    Worsley Navigable Levels 79
Cann Wood incline, Sparkwell 67
Cantrell incline, Ugborough 68
Carmears incline, Luxulyan valley, Lanlivery 89
Carn Grey Quarries tramway, St Austell 90
Caroline Wheal Prosper incline, West Buckfastleigh 57
Carpalla Tramway, St Stephen-in-Brannel 90
Chard
Chard Canal 32, 33
Chard Common incline 32, 33
Chard Reservoir 32, 33
Chard Canal 13

Chardstock
    Dorset Blue Lime and Cement Works 40
Chargot Wood, Langham Hill 48
Charterhouse Lead Works, Priddy 33
Chelsea Bridge 76, 83
Church Knowle
    Cocknowle inclines 40
Clandown Colliery incline 23
Clevedon
    Conygar Quarry incline 24
Clifton Rocks Railway 13, 17
Clifton Rocks Railway Trust 18
Clifton Suspension Bridge temporary incline 18
Coalport 11
Cocknowle inclines, Church Knowle 40
Colton Pits incline, Nettlecombe 48
Combe Hay
    Combe Hay Fullers Earth Mine incline 24
    Combe Hay incline, coal canal 23
Combe Martin
    Berry's Quarry 45
Comberow 47
Conkwell inclined plane 18
Conygar Quarry incline, Clevedon 24
Cornwall Archaeological Unit 98
Cornwall Council 86
Cornwall Mineral Railway 91
Croscombe
    Ham Wood Quarry 35
Cross quarry, near Axbridge 33
Cubitt, Sir William 32
D
Darby, Abraham 11
Dartmoor Forest
    Hensroost and Hooten Wheals 59
    Hexworthy Mine 59
Darwin, Erasmus 11
Davidstow
    Hendraburnick Quarry 86
    Davidstow airfield 87

Daws Castle Limekilns, Watchet 49
De Lank Quarry inclines 15, 83
Delabole Quarry, St Teath 84
Dening & Co of Chard 32
Devon County Council 63
Devon Friendship, Mary Tavy 57
Devon Gawton Co 74
Devon Great Consols, Gulworthy 73
Devon Great Consols Railway 74
    incline to Morwellham Quay 74
Dewerstone Quarries, Meavy 66
Dickens, Charles 39
Diesel engines
    Blackstone 87
Dorset Blue Lime and Cement Works 40
Dorset Lime Cement and Stone Co 41
Downhead Quarry, Downhead 34
Druxton Wharf 81
Duchy of Cornwall 96
Dulverton
    Forestry plantation 49
Dunball Portland Cement and Blue Lias Lime Works, 34
Dundas Aqueduct 19
Durfold China Clay Works, Blisland 85
E
East Bristol Collieries Ltd 19
East Cliff Railway, Bournemouth 41
East Cornwall Mineral Railway 72, 75, 76
Eastabrook, William 57
Ebbw Vale 47, 49
Ebbw Vale Company 47
Edyvean, John 97
Eliot, Sir George 43
Emily Mine, South Tawton 61
Exeter Brick and Tile Co 41
Exford
    Newland Quarry 52
Exmoor National Park 47
F
Farington Gurney
    Old Mills Colliery incline 28

Feeder Canal, Bristol 20
Fisherman's Walk railway, Bournemouth 41
Forestry plantation, Dulverton 49
Fowey
    Caffa Mill Pill-Penventinue incline 89
    Fowey Consols inclines 13, 89, 91
Foxcote Colliery incline, Hemington 25
Fremington Quay 50
Froward Point, Kingswear 65
Fullers Earth Union 24, 26
Fulton, Robert 11, 12, 80
G
Gawton Mine, Gulworthy 74
Geach, T. 96
Gibraltar Docks 83
Gill and Company 77
Gill and Rundle 79
Gillow Quarry, Tintagel 86
Gonamena Incline, Liskeard and
    Caradon Railway 86
Grand Western Canal 13, 34
Gravel Hill Mine, Perranzabuloe 91
Great Polgooth Mine, St Mewan 91
Great Rock Mine, Hennock 58
Great Torrington
    Rosemoor limekilns, near 55
Great Treviscoe Clay Works, St Dennis 91
Green, James 11, 12, 13, 32, 34, 53, 55, 80, 81
Greenhill Arsenic Works, Calstock 75
Grenville United Mines, Camborne 102
Greyfield Colliery incline, High Littleton 25
Greystone Wood mine incline 75
Gulworthy
    Bedford United mine 74
    Canal inclined plane to Morwellham
        Quay 79
    Devon Great Consols 73, 74
    Gawton Mine 74

Morwellham hydro-electric power
    station, 77
Morwellham Quay 79
Morwellham Quay Limekilns 77
Newquay Limekilns 78
Wheal Crebor 79
Gunnislake Clitters Mine, Calstock 75
Gwithian
    National Explosives Co 105
H
Hall, Sydney 32
Ham Wood Quarry, Croscombe 35
Ham Wood Quarry incline, Shepton
    Mallet 35
Handley, W. H. 26
Hanham
    Hanham Colliery incline 19
Happy Union Tin Mine, Pentewan valley 92
Hayle
    Angarrack Incline 102
    Hayle Railway 100, 102, 103
Haytor Iron Mines, Ilsington 58
Heard, William 50
Hemington
    Foxcote Colliery incline 25
Hendra Downs incline, St Dennis 13, 93
Hendraburnick Quarry, Davidstow 86
Hennock
    Great Rock Mine 58
Hexworthy Mine, Dartmoor Forest 59
High Littleton
    Greyfield Colliery incline 25
Highbridge Quay 50
    Hobbacott inclined plane, Launcells
        34, 54, 55, 81, 82, 83
Hodge, William Chapell 93
Hodge's Limekiln, Moorswater 93
Hodshill Fullers Earth Mine incline 26
Holne
    Holne Chase Mine 59
    Holne Moor Mine 61
    Ringleshuttes Mine 61

Hopkins & Co 94
Hopkins, Rice 47
Horse gins
    Bucks Mills, Woolfardisworthy 48
    Chargot Wood incline, Luxborough 48
    Clifton Suspension Bridge abutment
        incline 18
    Happy Union Tin Mine 92
    Ironmould Lane incline, Brislington 19
    Lusty Glaze, Newquay 97
    Mawgan Porth, Mawgan-in-Pydar 97
    Parrett Navigation incline, Langport 37
Wheal Trewavas, Breage 106
Huish Colliery incline, Kilmersdon 26
I
Ilminster
    Ilminster incline 32
Ilsington
    Bagtor Mine 57
    Haytor Iron Mines 58
    Stormsdown mine 62
Ironmould Lane incline, Brislington 19
Isaac, J. C. 94
K
Kalmeter, Henric 79
Kelly Mine, Bovey Tracey 59
Kelly Mine Preservation Society 59
Kennet and Avon Canal 19
Ketley inclined plane 11
Kilmar Railway 87
Kilmersdon
    Huish Colliery incline 26
    Kilmersdon Colliery incline 26
Kilmersdon Colliery, Norton-Radstock 26
Kingswear
    Brownstone Battery, Froward Point 65
Kit Hill Country Park, near Callington 77
Kit Hill Quarry, Stoke Climsland 76

Knight, Frederick 52
Knight, John 52
L
Lambeth Bridge 76, 83
Landewednack
    Lizard Lifeboat Station 104
Landkey
    Shebbear Pond 55
    Venn Pond 55
    Venn Quarries 55
Langport
    Parrett Navigation Incline 37
Lanivet
    Mulberry Open Work 94
    Wheal Prosper 99
Lanlivery
    Carmears Incline 89
    Treffry Viaduct 98
Lantern China Clay Pit, Bugle 93
Launcells
    Hobbacott Incline 81
Leats
    Chard Canal 32
    Fowey Consols 90, 91
    Molinnis-Fowey Consols 91, 98
    Tregargus China Stone Mills 98
Lee Moor Tramway 67
Lee Quarry, Marystow 59
Levant Mine, St Just in Penwith 104
Lezant
    Greystone Wood Manganese Mine, 75
Lifton
    Lifton Quarry incline 63
    Tinhay Quarry incline 63
Lighthouses
    Beachy Head 83
    Bishop Rock, Scilly Isles 76, 83
    Needles 83
    North Light, Lundy, incline 52
    Smalls 83
Limekilns
    Bucks Mills 48

Daws Castle, Watchet 49
Devoran Wharf 94
John Lyne's kiln, Moorswater 93
Meldon, Okehampton Hamlets 60
Morwellham Quay 77
Newquay, Gulworthy 78
Rosemoor 55
Tavistock 79, 94
William Hodge's Limekiln, Moorswater 93
Linkinhorne
    Gonamena incline 86
    West Caradon Mine 87
    West Phoenix Mine 87
Liskeard
    Limekilns at Moorswater 93
Liskeard and Caradon Railway 86, 87
    Gonamena incline 86
Lizard RNLI Lifeboat Station 104
Lockyer, Sir Norman 43
London & South Western Railway 63, 72
London Bridge 76
Londonderry Wharf 17
Long Ashton
    Clifton Suspension Bridge temporary incline 18
Long Grass Quarry, Tintagel 86
Lostwithiel
    Restormel Royal Iron Mine 95
Lowdon, John 11
Lower Conygre Colliery inclines, Timsbury 26
Lower Stone Quarry, Bridestowe 60
Lower Writhlington Colliery, Norton-Radstock 27
Ludlows Colliery incline, Norton Radstock 28
Lundy
    Granite quarry inclines 50
    North Light 52
    Quarry Beach 50
Lundy Granite Co 50

Lusty Glaze, Newquay 97
Luxborough
    Bearland Wood Mine 48
    Chargot Wood incline 48
    Nurcott Quarry 52
Luxulyan valley 89, 98
Lyne, John 94
Lyne's kiln, Moorswater 93
Lynton & Lynmouth Cliff Railway 13, 50
M
Mannings Brickworks, Parkstone 42
Mansfield, William 43
Marazion
    St Michaels Mount Cliff Railway 105
Marhamchurch incline 81
Marks, George Croydon 13, 17, 50, 65
Marsh Quarries, Swimbridge 51
Mary Tavy
    Devon Friendship 57
Marystow
    Lee Quarry 59
Mawgan-in-Pydar
    Mawgan Porth incline 97
St Columb Canal 97
Meavy
    Dewerstone Quarries 66
Meldon limekilns, Okehampton Hamlets 60
Mells
    Vobster Colliery incline 29
Merchants Railway, Isle of Portland 42
Merrifield incline, Bridgerule 81, 82
Michaelstow Quarry, Michaelstow 86
Miles Dock 20
Miles, William 20
Military railway, Steep Holm Island 36
Millaton estate 60, 62
Millwall Docks 76
Milton Quarry incline, Weston-super-Mare 28
Mines
    Axbridge Hill Iron Ochre Mine 32

Bagtor, Ilsington 57
Basset, Carn Brea 101
Bearland Wood 48
Bideford Black Culm Mine 45
Blackland, Withypool and Hawkridge 47
Botallack, St Just in Penwith 101
Braysdown Colliery, near Radstock 23
Bulkamore, Rattery 66
California Colliery, Oldland 17
Camerton New Pit, Camerton 23
Clandown Colliery, Norton Radstock 23
Colton Pits, Nettlecombe 48
Combe Hay Fullers Earth Mine 24
Devon Great Consols, Gulworthy 73
Fowey Consols, near St Blazey 91
Foxcote Colliery, Hemington 25
Gawton, Gulworthy 74
Gravel Hill, Perranzabuloe 91
Great Polgooth, St Mewan/St Ewe 91
Great Rock, Hennock 58
Grenville United, Troon 102
Greyfield Colliery, High Littleton 25
Gunnislake Clitters, Calstock 75
Hanham Colliery, Hanham 19
Happy Union, Pentewan valley 92
Haytor Iron Mine, Ilsington 58
Hexworthy Mine, Dartmoor Forest 59
Hodshill Fullers Earth Mine, South Stoke 26
Holne Chase 59
Huish Colliery, Kilmersdon 26
Kelly, Bovey Tracey 59
Kilmersdon Colliery, Norton-Radstock 26
Levant, St Just in Penwith 104
Lower Conygre Colliery, Timsbury 26
Lower Writhlington Colliery, Norton-Radstock 27

Ludlows Colliery, Norton-Radstock 28
Moorwood, Moretonhampstead 61
Mulberry Open Work, Lanivet 94
New Moorewood Colliery, Ashwick 28
Old Mills and Springfield Collieries, Farington Gurney 28
Par Consols, St Blazey 95
Pensford Colliery, Stanton Drew 28
Pepperdon, Moretonhampstead 61
Ramsley, South Tawton 61
Restormel Royal Iron Mine, Lostwithiel 95
Ringleshuttes, Holne 61
Salisbury Colliery, Paulton 28
Tyning Colliery, Norton-Radstock 29
Vobster Colliery, Vobster, Mells 29
Wellsway Colliery, Norton-Radstock 29
Welton Hill Colliery, Norton-Radstock 30
West Caradon, Minions 87
West Phoenix, Minions, 87
Wheal Crebor, Gulworthy 79
Wheal Friendly, St Agnes 106
Wheal Owles, St Just in Penwith 106
Wheal Prosper, Lanivet 99
Wheal Trewavas, Breage 106
Withy Mills Colliery, Timsbury 30
Monkleigh
    Ridd incline 53
Moorwood, Moretonhampstead 61
Moretonhampstead
    Moorwood mine 61
    Pepperdon mine 61
Morwellham hydro-electric power station, Gulworthy 77
Morwellham inclined planes 71
Morwellham Quay, Gulworthy 74, 79

Morwellham Quay Limekilns, Gulworthy 77

Muirhill quarry incline, Winsley 20
Mulberry Open Work, Lanivet 94
Mushet, Robert 10
N
National Explosives Company, Gwithian 105
Netham Chemical Works incline 20
Nettlecombe
    Colton Pits incline 48
New Moorewood Colliery incline, Ashwick 28
Newland Quarry, Exford 52
Newnes, Sir George 13, 50, 65
Newquay
    Newquay Harbour incline 13, 94
    St Columb Canal 90, 97
Newquay Limekilns, Gulworthy 78
Nobel, Alfred 105
North Curry
    Wrantage incline 32
North Light incline, Lundy 52
North Tamerton
    Tamerton incline 81
Norton-Radstock
    Braysdown Colliery incline 23
    Clandown Colliery incline 23
    Kilmersdon Colliery 26
    Lower Writhlington Colliery 27
    Ludlows Colliery incline 28
    Wellsway Colliery incline 29
    Welton Hill Colliery incline 30
Nurcott Quarry, Luxborough 52
O
Oakhampton Quarry, Wiveliscombe 52
Oil engines
    Blackstone 59
Okehampton Hamlets
    Meldon limekilns 60
Old Mills colliery incline, Farington Gurney 28
Oldland
    California Colliery incline 17
Olver, Thomas, & Co 99

P

Padstow
  Stepper Point Quarry 98
Palmer, Jack 62
Palmer, Samborn 11
Palmerston, Lord 36
Pancrasweek
  Vealand incline 81
Par Canal 89
Par Consols, St Blazey 13, 95
Par Harbour 89, 94
Paradise Bottom Tramway, Abbots Leigh 20
Parkandillack clay works 93
Parknoweth Tramway 106
Parkstone
  Mannings Brickworks 42
  Omnium Factory (Brickworks) 42
Parkyn, Frank 85, 86
Parrett Navigation incline, Langport 37
Paulton
  Salisbury Colliery incline 28
  Salisbury Colliery Tramway 28
PBWC Architects 97
Pease, William 13, 95
Penponds incline, Camborne 102
Pensford Colliery incline, Stanton Drew 28
Pepperdon, Moretonhampstead 61
Perranzabuloe
  Gravel Hill Mine 91
Perry Spear and Company 78
Petrol engines
  Ruston 105
Plym Bridge Woods estate 69
Plym River Slab and Slate Company 69
Plymouth
  Rumple Quarry 69
Plymouth and Dartmoor Railway 67, 69
Port Gaverne 84
Port Isaac 84
  breakwater 87
Portesham Quarry, Portesham 43

Porthoustock
  Batty's Point silo 105
Portland Breakwater 39
Portland, Isle of
  Admiralty Breakwater railway 39
  Castletown Pier 42
  Merchants Railway 42
  Priory Corner 42
Portreath Harbour - World Heritage Site 102
Portreath incline 102
Priddy
  Charterhouse Lead Works 33
  St Cuthbert's Lead Works 37
Puriton
  Dunball Portland Cement and Blue Lias Lime Works 34
Putney Bridge 76, 83

Q

Quarries
  Admiralty Quarries, Portland 39
  Alder, Thrushelton 57
  Bailey's, Bampton 45
  Bathampton Down 17
  Belstone 57
  Berry's, Combe Martin 45
  Boscastle slate quarry, Trevalga 81
  Bridford 57
  Carn Grey, St Austell 90
  Coaxdon, Chardstock 40
  Combe Down, Bath 21
  Conkwell, Winsley 18, 19
  Conygar, Clevedon 24, 25
  Cross, near Axbridge 33
  De Lank, St Breward 15, 83
  Delabole, St Teath 84, 85
  Dewerstone, Meavy 66
  Downhead 34
  Ham Wood, Shepton Mallet 35
  Heard's, Lundy 50
  Hendraburnick, Davidstow 86
  Immosthay, Portland 42
  King Barrow, Portland 42

  Kit Hill, Stoke Climsland 76, 77
  Lee, Marystow 59, 60
  Lifton 63
  Lower Stone, Bridestowe 60
  Lundy Island Granite Quarries 50
  Marsh, Swimbridge 51
  Michaelstow 86
  Milton, Weston-super-Mare 28
  Muirhill, Winsley 18, 20
  Newland, Exford 52
  Nurcott, Luxborough 52
  Oakhampton, Wiveliscombe 52
  Orchard, Luxulyan 95
  Portesham 43
  Portland stone quarries 38
  Rumple, Plym valley 69
  Scatter Rocks, Bridford 61
  Sourton, Bridestowe 62
  South Tawton 62
  St Keverne 105
  Stepper Point, Padstow 98
  Swell Tor, Walkhampton 63
  Tinhay, Lifton 63
  Torr, Woodleigh 69
  Tout, Portland 42
  Tregildrans, St Kew 87
  Tregongeeves, St Ewe 99
  Venn Quarries, Landkey 55
  Waycroft, Portland 42
  Wilminstone, Tavistock 63
  Withies Croft, Portland 39

R

Rails
  cast iron 10, 20, 77
  plate 19, 30, 77
  steel 10
  tramplates 30
  wooden 10, 20
  wrought iron 10
Railways
  Abbotsbury branch 43
  Ashburton branch 66
  Babbacombe Cliff Lift 65

Bristol & Exeter 34
Bristol and North Somerset Railway
    25
Bristol-Radstock 28, 30
Cornwall Mineral Railway 91
Devon Great Consols 73, 74
East Cornwall Mineral Railway 72,
    75, 76
Exe Valley branch 45
Ffestiniog 10
Frome-Radstock 26
Great Western 37, 68
Hallatrow-Limpley Stoke 26
Hayle Railway 100, 102
Heathfield to Exeter 61
Kilmar 87
Launceston branch 60, 63
Lee Moor Tramway 67
Liskeard and Caradon 86, 87
London & South Western 63, 72
Lynton & Lynmouth Cliff Railway 50
Meldon Viaduct 60
Plymouth and Dartmoor 63, 67, 69
Princetown branch 63
Somerset & Dorset 23, 28, 35
St Dennis branch 91
Steep Holm Military Railway 36, 37
Teign Valley branch 62
Treffry tramway 89
Tregantle Military Railway 78
West Cornwall 103
West Somerset Mineral Railway 47
Weston, Clevedon and Portishead
    Light Railway 24
Yealmpton branch 69
Ralph Allen's Tramway, Bath 21
Ramsley Mine, South Tawton 61
Rattery
    Bulkamore Mine 66
Redlake Tramway, Ugborough 68
Redruth
    Basset Mines, Carn Brea 101
    Tresavean incline 102

Rennie, John 13
Restormel Iron Mining Co 96
Restormel Royal Iron Mine, Lostwithiel
    95
Reynolds, William 8, 11, 12
Ridd incline, Monkleigh 53, 54
Ringleshuttes Mine, Holne 61
RNLI Lizard Lifeboat Station 104
RNLI Padstow Lifeboat Station, 97
Roads Reconstruction (1934) Ltd 61
Robinson, George 60
Rogers, Joseph 103
Rolle Canal 13, 53, 54
Rolle, Denys 53
Rosemoor limekilns, near Great
    Torrington 55
Rosemoor limekilns, St Giles in the
    Wood 55
Rowe, Captain John 101
Rowes and Crocker 62
Royal Engineers, The 65, 78
Rumple Quarry incline, Plymouth 69
S
Salcombe Regis
    Salcombe Hill incline 43
    South Down 43
Salisbury Colliery incline, Paulton 28
Salisbury Colliery Tramway, Paulton 28
Saltburn Cliff Lift, Redcar 13, 50
Scatter Rocks, Bridford 61
Scatter Rocks Macadams Ltd 61
Scraesdon incline, Tregantle Military
    Railway 78
Sennen Cove, St Just in Penwith 105
Shepton Mallet
    Ham Wood Quarry incline 35
Singapore Docks 83
Somerset & Dorset Railway 28, 35
Somerset Mineral Syndicate 48
Somersetshire Coal Canal 22, 26, 28,
    30
Somersetshire Coal Canal Tramway 23
Sourton Quarry, Bridestowe 62

South Hams Brickworks 69
South Stoke
    Hodshill Fullers Earth Mine incline 26
South Tawton
    Ramsley Mine 61
    South Tawton Quarry incline 62
Sparkwell
    Cann Wood incline 67
    Torycombe incline 67
Springfield Colliery incline, Farington
    Gurney 28
St Agnes
    Trevaunance Combe 106
    Trevellas Combe 106
    Wheal Friendly 106
St Austell
    Carn Grey Quarries tramway 90
    Wheal Martyn 99
St Blazey
    Par Consols 95
St Breward
    De Lank Quarry 83
St Columb Canal 88, 97
St Cuthbert's Lead Works, Priddy 37
St Decumans
    Daws Castle limekilns 49
St Dennis
    Great Treviscoe Clay Works 91
    Hendra Downs incline 93
St Eval airfield 87
St Ewe
    Tregongeeves Quarry 99
St Giles in the Wood
    Rosemoor limekilns 55
St Just in Penwith
    Botallack Mine 101
    Levant Mine 104
    Sennen Cove 105
    Wheal Boys 106
    Wheal Drea 106
    Wheal Owles 106
St Keverne Quarries 105

St Kew
  Tregildrans quarry incline 87
St Merryn
  Padstow RNLI Lifeboat Station 97
St Mewan
  Great Polgooth Mine 91
St Michaels Mount Cliff Railway,
  Marazion 105
St Stephen-in-Brannel
  Carpalla Tramway 90
  Tregargus China Stone Mills and
    inclines 98
St Teath
  Delabole Quarry 84
Stanton Drew
  Pensford Colliery incline 28
Steam engines, stationary
  Angarrack Incline 102
  Blackland Mine, Withypool 47
  Brendon Incline, at 47
  Brown & May 34
  Calstock Incline 72
  Charterhouse Lead Works, Priddy 33
  Davey Paxman 68
  Delabole 85
  Devon Great Consols Railway incline
    74
  Downhead Quarry 34
  Foxcote Colliery, Hemington 25
  Gravel Hill Mine, at 91
  Gunnislake Clitters Mine, Calstock
    75
  Hendra Downs 93
  Lantern China Clay Pit 93
  Ludlows Colliery, Norton-Radstock
    28
  Mannings Brickworks, Parkstone 42
  Marsh Quarries, Swimbridge 51
  Netham Chemical Works 20
  New Moorewood Colliery, Ashwick
    28
  Newquay Harbour incline 94

Oakhampton Quarry, Wiveliscombe
  52
Old Mills Colliery, Farington Gurney
  28
Par Consols 95
Pearce's Whim, Botallack 101
Pensford Colliery, Stanton Drew 28
Portreath incline 102
Redlake Tramway, Ugborough 68
Robey 47
Rumple Quarry, Plym valley 69
Ruston and Hornsby 87
Vobster Colliery, Mells 29
Wheal Emma, Devon Great Consols
  73
Steep Holm
  Military railway 36, 37
Steer Point Brickworks, Brixton 69
Stepper Point Quarry, Padstow 98
Stoke Climsland
  Kit Hill Quarry 76
Stormsdown, Ilsington 62
Swell Tor Quarries, Walkhampton 63
Swimbridge
  Marsh Quarries 51

T
Tamar Coal, Manure & General
  Mercantile Co 72
Tamar Lake 82
Tamerton incline, North Tamerton 81
Tavistock
  Tavistock Limekilns 79
  Wilminstone Quarry 63
Tavistock Canal 77, 79
  inclined plane to Morwellham Quay
    79
Taylor, John 12, 79
Taylor, John, & Sons 59, 96
Teign Valley branch railway 62
Thornfalcon incline, Thornfalcon 32
Thrushelton
  Alder Quarry 57

Timsbury
  Lower Conygre Colliery inclines 26
  Withy Mills Colliery incline, 30
Tinhay Quarry, Lifton 63
Tintagel
  Gillow Quarry 86
  Long Grass Quarry 86
Tom, Leonard 87
Torbay Council 65
Torquay
  Babbacombe Cliff Lift 65
  Boots the Chemist 65
Torr Quarry, Woodleigh 69
Torrington Canal 53
Torycombe incline, Sparkwell 67
Tramroads
  Crowns, Botallack Mine 101
  Dramway 17
  Salisbury Colliery, Paulton 28
Tramways
  Carn Grey Quarries 90
  Carpella Tramway 90
  Parknoweth 106
  Quarry Tramway, St Keverne 105
  Restormel Royal Iron Mine 95
  Somersetshire Coal Canal 23, 30
  Treffry tramway 89, 94
Treffry, J. T. 13, 88, 89, 91, 94, 95
Treffry Viaduct 13, 89, 98
Tregantle Military Railway 78
Tregargus China Stone Mills, St Stephen-
  in-Brannel 98
Tregildrans Quarry, St Kew 87
Tregongeeves Quarry, St Ewe 99
Tresavean incline, Redruth 102
Trevalga
  Boscastle Slate Quarry 81
Turbines, water
  Chard Common incline 32
  Kelly Mine, Bovey Tracey 59
  Whitelaw and Stirrat 32
Turner's Tower 25

Tywardreath and Par
  Fowey Consols 91

U

Ugborough
  Redlake Tramway 68
University College, London 12

V

Vealand incline, Pancrasweek 81
Venn Quarries, Landkey 55
Verne incline, Portland 43
Vobster Colliery incline,
  Mells/Leigh-upon-Mendip 29

W

Wacker Quay 78
Walkhampton
  Swell Tor Quarries 63
Wareham Cement Company 40
Watchet
  Daws Castle limekilns 49
Waterloo Bridge 76
Waterwheels
  Bagtor Mine, Ilsington 57
  Caffa Mill Pill, Fowey 89
  Caroline Wheal Prosper, West
    Buckfastleigh 57
  Dorset Blue Lime and Cement
    Works, Chardstock 40
  Durfold China Clay Works 85
  Ilminster incline 32
  John Lyne's kiln, Moorswater 93
  Lower Stone Quarry, Bridestowe 60
  Marhamchurch incline 81
  Merrifield incline, Bridgerule 81, 82
  Morwellham Quay Limekilns 77
  Newland Quarry, Exford 52
  Newquay limekilns, Gulworthy 78
  Nurcott Quarry, Luxborough 52
  Rumple Quarry, Plym valley 69
  Sourton Quarry, Bridestowe 62
  Tamartown incline, Werrington 81
  Tamerton incline, North Tamerton
    81

Tavistock Canal inclined plane,
  Morwellham 79
Tavistock limekilns 79
Thornfalcon incline 32
Vealand incline, Pancrasweek 81
Venn Quarries, Landkey 55
Wheal Crebor, Gulworthy 79
William Hodge's Limekiln 93
Wrantage incline, North Curry 32
Waycroft Quarries, Portland 43
Waygood Otis Company 65
Weldon, Robert 22
Wellisford inclined plane, Wellington
  Without 34
Wellsway Colliery incline, Norton-
  Radstock 29
Welton Hill Colliery incline, Norton-
  Radstock 30
Werrington
  Tamartown incline 81
West Buckfastleigh
  Caroline Wheal Prosper 57
West Caradon Mine, Linkinhorne 87
West Cliff Railway, Bournemouth 41
West Cornwall Railway 103
West Devon Council 63
West Phoenix Mine, Linkinhorne 87
West Somerset Mineral Railway 47, 48
Western Counties Brick Company 69
Weston, Clevedon and Portishead Light
Railway 24
Weston-super-Mare
  Milton Quarry incline 28
Wheal Crebor, Gulworthy 79
Wheal Emma, Gulworthy 73
Wheal Emma New Shaft, Gulworthy 73
Wheal Friendly, St Agnes 106
Wheal Josiah, Gulworthy 73
Wheal Martyn China Clay Museum and
Country Park 99
Wheal Owles, St Just in Penwith 106
Wheal Prosper, Lanivet 99

Wheal Trewavas, Breage 106
Wheaton, William 40
Whitelaw and Stirrat water turbine 32
Williams, Henry 11
Wilminstone Quarry, Tavistock 63
Winsley
  Muirhill quarry incline 20
Withers, R. B. 20
Withies Croft Quarries, Portland 39
Withy Mills Colliery incline, Timsbury 30
Withypool
  Blackland Mine 47

Wiveliscombe
  Oakhampton Quarry 52
Woodleigh
  Torr Quarry 69
Woolfardisworthy
  Bucks Mills 48
Woollcombe, John Morth 57
Wrantage incline, North Curry 32
Wyndham estate 49

Y

Yelland, Abel 82

Z

Zawn Brinny incline, Levant Mine 104